WATER, SOIL AND THE PLANT

Science in Horticulture Series

General Editor: Professor L. Broadbent, University of Bath

This series of texts has been designed for students on courses in horticulture at the Higher National Certificate or Diploma level, but care has been taken to ensure that they are not too specialised for lower-level courses, nor too superficial for university work.

All the contributors to the series have had experience in both the horticultural industry and education. Consequently, the books have a strong practical flavour which should reinforce their value as textbooks and also make them of interest to a wide audience, including growers and farmers, extension officers, research workers, workers in the agrochemical, marketing and allied industries, and the many gardeners who are interested in the science behind their hobby.

The authors are all British, but they have illustrated their books with examples drawn from many countries. As a result the texts should be of value to English-speaking students of horticulture throughout the world.

The maner of watering with a Pumpe in a Tubbe.

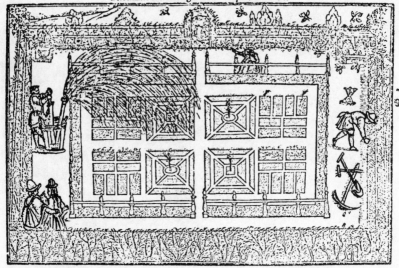

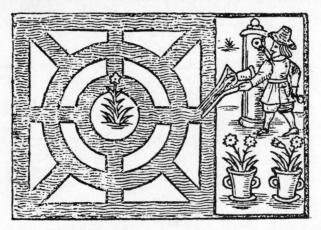

There be some which use to water their beds with great Squirts, made of Tin; in drawing up the water, and setting the Squirt to the brest, that by force squirted upward, the water in the breaking may fall as drops of raine on the plants, which sundry times like squirted on the beds, doth sufficiently feed the plants with moisture.

Frontispiece: Elizabethan irrigation, furrow and sprinkle from *The Gardeners Labyrinth* (Anon.) 1651

WATER, SOIL AND THE PLANT

E. J. WINTER

Head of Irrigation Section
National Vegetable Research Station
Wellesbourne, Warwickshire

MACMILLAN

First published 1974 by
THE MACMILLAN PRESS LTD
London and Basingstoke
Associated companies in New York Dublin
Melbourne Johannesburg and Madras

SBN 333 12948 2

Set I.B.M. by
GEORGE OVER LIMITED, LONDON AND RUGBY

Printed in Great Britain by
Whitstable Litho Straker Brothers Ltd

All the rivers run into the sea, yet the sea is not full; unto the place whence the rivers come thither they return again.

Ecclesiastes 1:7

CONTENTS

Frontispiece   *facing page* iii

Preface   xi

Introduction   xiii

1 THE WATER BALANCE   1
   Annual rainfall distribution   1
   Precipitation rate   8
   Evaporation   8
   Dew   8
   Drainage   9
   The water balance   9
   Water need maps   9
   Measuring the water balance   11

2 WATER SUPPLIES FOR HORTICULTURE'   23
   Sources of water; pumping machinery   24
   Abstraction points   24
   Cross-stream dams and off-stream pounds   25
   Artificial lakes and reservoirs   26
   Wells and boreholes   26
   Public water supplies   26
   Land drains   27
   Underground recharge   28
   Estuarine barrages   29
   The sea as a possible source of irrigation water   29
   Water quality   30
   Dissolved salts   31
   Accumulation of salts in the surface soil   31
   Assessing water supplies   32
   Regulating water abstraction   34

3 THE SOIL RESERVOIR   35
   Soil series   35
   Soil texture   35
   Soil horizons   35
   Drainage   36
   Pore space   37
   Soil water potentials   37
   Matric potential, or suction   38

Osmotic potential, or suction 38
pF 39
Soil moisture characteristic 40
The lower limit of available water (permanent wilting point) 41
The upper limit of available water (field capacity) 42
Available water capacity 43
Apparent specific gravity, or bulk density 48
The influence of structure on available water capacity 49
The energy concept of soil water 49
Measurement of soil moisture parameters 50

4 MOVEMENT OF WATER IN SOIL 61
Erosion 61
Capping 62
Water movement in saturated soil 64
The wetted front 65
The water table 65
Impeded drainage 66
Water movement in unsaturated soil 66
Evaporation from soil 67
Measurement of soil water movement 67

5 THE HYDROLOGICAL STRUCTURE OF VASCULAR PLANTS 71
The water-conducting vessels 71
Roots 71
The root system 72
Stems and foliage 73
Stomata 74
The 'plumbing' system 74
General conformation 74
Organs which produce mechanical movement 76
Measurement of stomatal aperture 76
Measurement of stem flow 78

6 ENTRY OF WATER INTO THE PLANT 81
Entry of water into the root 81
Root pressure 82
Supply of water to the root 83
Growth of roots towards water 84
The exploitation of soil available water 84
Temporary wilting 88
Measurement of entry of water into the plant 88
Demonstration and measurement of root pressure 89

7 WATER WITHIN THE PLANT 91
Transpiration rates 91
The water status of plant tissues 92

Water stress	93
Results of reduction in plant water potential	94
Effects on stomata	94
Gross physiological effects	95
Effects on growth and development	96
Transport	96
Measurement of factors associated with movement of water within the plant	97

8 MOVEMENT OF WATER OUT OF THE PLANT–SOIL SYSTEM	101
Boundary layer	101
Empirical determinations of evaporation	101
Estimation of evaporation from physical measurements	102
Potential and actual transpiration	104
Root constant or crop constant	105
Incomplete crop cover	106
Soil moisture deficit	106
Depletion of available water	106
The significance of transpiration	107
Measurement of transpiration	109
Measurement and estimation of soil moisture deficit	109

9 HORTICULTURAL IMPLICATIONS	113
Effects of water stress on crop plants	113
Limited irrigation	116
Water stress and produce quality	116
Water stress and growth	118
Development of water stress	119
Manipulating available water capacity	119
Water tables	121
Soil water conservation	121
Evaporation reduction in practice	122
Exploitation of soil reservoir	122
Glasshouse crop irrigation	124
Outdoor irrigation	127
Water, soil and the plant	128

Appendix The Penman formula	129
Bibliography	133
Index	137

PREFACE

This book has been written to fill the needs of students taking either the National Diploma in Horticulture or the new Higher National Diploma in Horticulture which has been introduced recently. It should also prove useful to students in universities taking degree courses in the subject. It draws on information and opinions collected by the author during thirty-five years of collaboration with growers, planters, advisers, scientists and amateur horticulturists in many temperate and tropical countries.

Because of the immense number of people involved it is impracticable to acknowledge them all by name, but I wish to express my grateful thanks to every one; it is a splendid characteristic of the horticultural industry that almost every individual is willing and anxious to share his knowledge and experience for the common good, and especially for the education of newcomers. There are few trade secrets in our industry. Without such generous pooling of knowledge this book could not have been written.

For much the same reasons I have not attempted to produce formal references to original authors for each scientific fact quoted; long lists of references can be daunting to the young student. Instead I have given suggestions for further reading including review papers which contain detailed lists of references for those who require them.

I wish to thank Professor Wright, Director of the National Vegetable Research Station, and my professional colleagues especially Drs Salter, Stanhill, Sale, D. Drew, Cox and Rowse, Messrs Williams, R. Drew, Stone and McKee, Miss Lucy Blackwall and Mrs Joyce Steckel for the use of data and ideas accumulated during our long service together, Miss Jenny Wright who prepared most of the photographs and Miss Angela Rose for her long-suffering secretarial help.

My wife also deserves special mention for good-humouredly accepting the domestic upheaval entailed in writing a book in one's 'spare time'.

Welford on Avon   E. J. W.

INTRODUCTION

Everyone knows that plants need water in order to survive, and horticulturists know that to ensure maximum growth they must never allow their plants to suffer from water shortage. It therefore comes as no surprise to the layman to learn that ordinary plants consist of over 90 per cent water; however what may be surprising is that under normal temperate summer conditions a square metre of vegetation transpires about two litres per day or nearly half a gallon per square yard. A mature lettuce plant transpires more than half its own weight of water every sunny day.

The object of this book is to discuss why this happens, how it happens and what use it is to the plant and hence to the horticulturist. The book is not a treatise on irrigation practice; such information is given in the publications cited on page 135.

Water reaches the soil mainly as rain; some is stored in the soil itself, some drains down through the topsoil into lower layers while if the soil is already saturated some may flow off the surface into drains and streams. Of the water in the soil a portion evaporates from the soil surface and a portion is taken up by the roots of plants and is evaporated, or transpired, from their foliage into the atmosphere. This circulation of water from the atmosphere into the soil and back to the atmosphere comprises the hydrological cycle and is dealt with in chapter 1.

Water supplies for plants are described in chapter 2. These are derived mainly from precipitation, from the water table or from upward or lateral movement of water within the soil. Supplementary water for irrigation may be obtained from streams, lakes, ground-water wells or deep boreholes. The quality of this water sometimes gives cause for concern as it may be more or less saline or contain harmful pollutants such as surfactants (detergents) or toxic materials derived from industrial wastes.

Chapter 3 describes the nature of soil, which consists of various sized particles of inorganic and organic matter having irregular shapes and therefore not fitting closely together. The voids thus left may be filled with air or water and constitute the all-important soil reservoir. The capacity of this reservoir is greatly influenced by the soil texture, that is, its particle size spectrum.

It follows from what has been said of the entry of water into the soil and its removal by plants, drainage and evaporation that the soil water is not static; it is in a continuous state of movement downwards or sideways in mass flow or upwards by capillary action. The rates of these movements are largely controlled by the soil texture and by local differences in soil moisture content which result from surface evaporation, precipitation and uptake into roots. The dynamic state of the soil water is discussed in chapter 4.

Chapter 5 gives structural details of those parts of vascular plants involved in the transfer of water from the soil into the atmosphere, namely the root system which has tissues capable of absorbing liquid water and transferring it into the xylem vessels, the xylem tube system itself, and the cells in the foliage which receive the water from the upper ends of the vessels and evaporate it from their surfaces into the intercellular spaces whence it moves back into the atmosphere mainly through the stomata. Entry of water into the plant and its relationship with the entry of solutes and the functioning of the root system as a whole in exploiting soil available water are described in chapter 6.

Chapter 7 discusses water within the plant, the development of internal water stress and its effect on growth, and the mechanism by which water is raised to the tops of the tallest trees. Internal water stress affects the plant in many ways and can have disastrous effects on growth and yield. Transpiration, the movement of water out of the plant into the atmosphere, is mainly a passive process whose maximum rate depends upon the quantity of energy available from sunlight and from advective sources and whose actual rate is governed by factors such as resistance to water uptake from the soil, resistance to movement within the plant, and the temperature, humidity and motion of the air surrounding the foliage. Chapter 8 is concerned with the loss of water from the foliage and with methods for estimating transpiration from meteorological observations and hence the desirable amounts and timing of supplementary watering.

The bad effects of water stress on crop growth and production can be countered by measures for improving the structure and texture of the soil, for conserving water in the soil reservoir, manipulating the water table and augmenting natural rainfall by judicious irrigation; the practical application of such measures is discussed in the final chapter 9. A section of this chapter deals with the special problems of meeting the water needs of plants grown under protection such as that provided by glasshouses, often in pots or other containers. Here there is usually no contribution from rain, evaporative conditions may be severe and the soil reservoir comparatively small; the general principles are the same as those apertaining to open fields but the methods of applying them are different.

In some climates irrigation enables crops to be grown in otherwise unproductive places or seasons of the year; in less rigorous climates supplementary watering can increase yield and quality out of all proportion to its cost. However in each of these circumstances haphazard and indiscriminate irrigation can be expensive, unproductive and even harmful. It is the purpose of this book to expound the principles underlying the profitable use of the soil reservoir in exploiting natural water resources and supplementing these with irrigation only when this is economically worthwhile.

Throughout the book descriptions have been given of methods and instruments for measuring factors associated with the movement of water in soil and plants. Many of the devices can be made from comparatively simple components and the exercise will help the student to appreciate the principles involved. Most of these instruments were originally devised for research and if in difficulty the student should refer to the publication cited. As indicated in the text, a few have been adapted for use in horticulture but the busy grower is understandably reluctant to adopt devices which need frequent attention and for this reason good watering principles which depend on instrumentation have not been generally applied in practice. The student might well consider ways of simplifying appropriate research devices while still retaining sufficient accuracy for application in practical horticulture.

THE WATER BALANCE

The ultimate source of water for plants is precipitation; rain falling upon soil penetrates it at a rate depending upon the physical properties of that particular soil; snow and hail do the same after melting. If the rate of rainfall or the rate of production of water by melting exceeds the infiltration rate, then surface runoff occurs and the excess water drains into streams and eventually reaches the sea. That water which penetrates the soil replenishes the soil reservoir and when this is filled to capacity (see chapter 3) the surplus drains through into the aquifers. These are strata such as sand or chalk which can hold substantial quantities of recoverable water. Water held in the soil reservoir is drawn into plant roots and up their stems to be evaporated from the leaves back into the atmosphere, where it rejoins water evaporated from the sea, lakes and rivers and from the surface of wet soil. This so-called hydrological cycle (figure 1.2) depends for its continuance upon energy derived from the sun's radiation and as will be shown in later chapters its rate is governed largely by meteorological factors.

ANNUAL RAINFALL DISTRIBUTION

Different parts of the world may be characterised according to the distribution of their rainfall. Northern and Central India have most of their rain in summer, the Mediterranean in winter whereas equatorial Africa and the United Kingdom have rain all the year round. The amount of sunshine and the resultant ruling temperature ultimately govern which crops can be grown in the open (though additionally some species require peculiar soil types; tea will grow only in acid soil) but whatever the crop, it must have water and thus the agricultural exploitation of a locality depends upon adequate rainfall or supplies of irrigation water, themselves derived from precipitation.

Figure 1.1 shows the world seasonal rainfall distribution in broad terms; the usefulness of this water depends on factors other than its annual total quantity. Firstly the water is required by crops during their growing season, which is dictated by sunshine and sometimes daylength; thus in a zone of winter-only precipitation there must be adequate water storage in aquifers, in artificial reservoirs or in the soil itself for subsequent use by crops in summer. In Kubishevsk Province (USSR), west of the Urals, there is only about 35 mm rain per month during the cereal growing season; during the winter precipitation is less than 20 mm per month but because

2

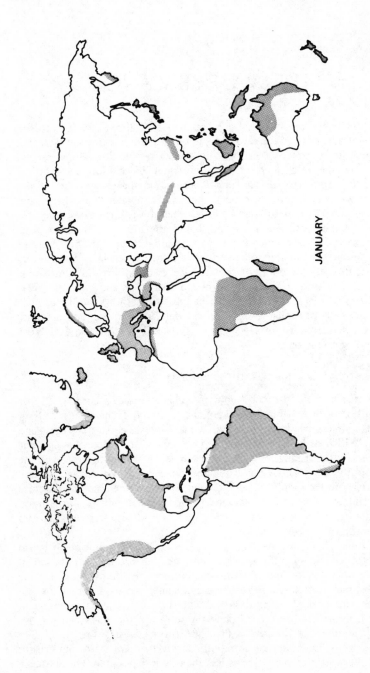

JANUARY

Figure 1.1

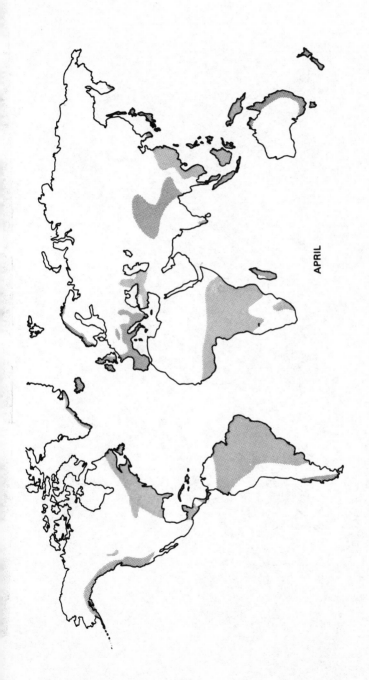

APRIL

Figure 1.1

4

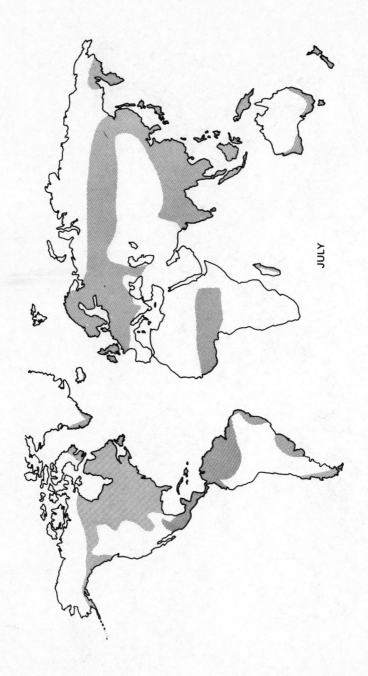

JULY

Figure 1.1

5

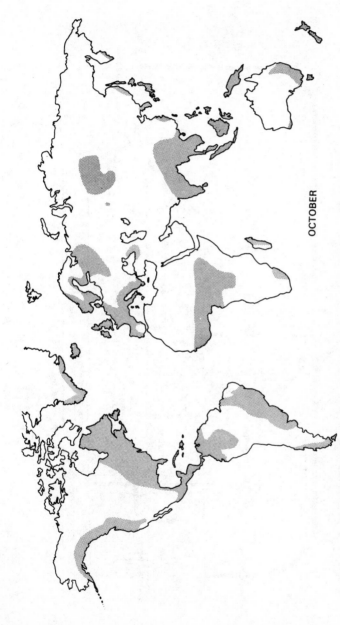

OCTOBER

Figure 1.1 Seasonal distribution of precipitation exceeding 50 mm (2 in) per month (shaded areas).
A few coastal-temperate, equatorial and island zones receive adequate rain all the year round; most areas receive their main rainfall only in the warm season or in the cold season.
Accurate delineation is impracticable at this small scale; for precise information the reader should consult a conventional large-scale atlas.

6

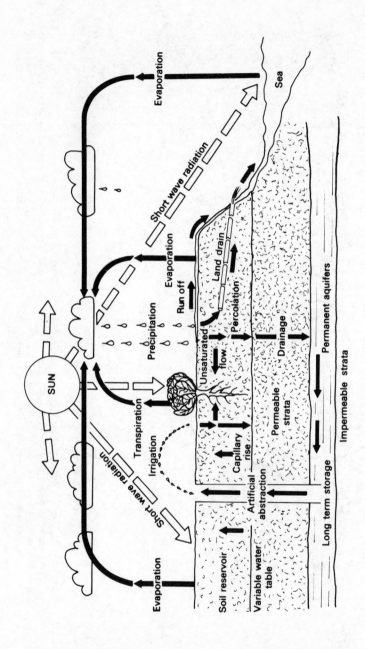

Figure 1.2   The hydrological cycle.

the soil surface thaws before deeper layers the resulting impeded drainage causes sufficient accumulation of water to replenish the soil fully and to meet crop needs the following summer. This is an example of *natural* bulk storage of water. In southern France also, winter rainfall is stored for irrigating orchards during the rainless summer but here the reservoirs are artificial. In contrast the Assam rice crop derives its whole water requirement from monsoon rain falling during the growing season itself.

In the UK, although monthly precipitation is fairly uniform throughout the year, evaporation usually exceeds rainfall during the summer growing season (table 1.1) and the resulting soil moisture stress almost invariably reduces growth. Under such conditions irrigation of almost any crop can improve its yield, though as will be seen later the cost

Table 1.1

Evaporation, precipitation and drainage measured in Central England 1969

	Rainfall (mm)	Evaporation (transpiration) from grass abundantly supplied with water	Surplus of rainfall over evaporation i.e. drainage	Surplus of evaporation over rainfall i.e. deficit
Jan	68	16	52	
Feb	46	4	42	
Mar	76	20	56	
Apr	72	34	38	
May	79	42	37	
Jun	61	80		19
Jul	52	88		36
Aug	27	61		34
Sep	39	53		14
Oct	20	23		3
Nov	108	14	94	
Dec	53	1	52	

These parameters are usually expressed in millimetres or inches, being the depth to which the stated quantity of water would inundate a horizontal surface on which it had fallen.

Recalculated from data of R. Blundell (1970) (private communication) Stockbridge House Experimental Horticulture Station, Ministry of Agriculture Fisheries and Food.

may outweigh the value of the extra produce. Moisture stress may be long-term and seasonal as in the Mediterranean, or it may be short-term and sporadic as in the UK where fifteen days without rain is officially classed as 'drought'. Here rainless periods of only one or two weeks have been shown to reduce crop growth and irrigation during such short periods of moisture stress can increase yield.

PRECIPITATION RATE

In temperate zones ordinary rain falls at the rate of about 1–2 mm per hour; precipitation from a Scotch mist is only a fraction of this rate. In the UK precipitation at 25 mm (nearly half the average monthly rainfall) per hour is not uncommon but such storms are usually of very short duration. In August 1952 a deluge of 175 mm in seven hours falling on already-saturated moorland caused the disastrous Lynmouth flood. In contrast, on the southern escarpment of the 2500 m Khasi Mountains of north-east India, where annual rainfall exceeds 10 000 mm (400 in) *all falling in six months*, a precipitation rate of many inches per hour is commonly sustained for many hours. There the author once measured 180 mm (7.5 in) of rain in half an hour.

The agricultural significance of precipitation rate lies in its relation to the rate at which the local soil can accept the water, that is, its characteristic infiltration rate. Infiltration rates range from 800 mm per minute for a sandy soil to only 20 mm for a clay. Water falling in excess of the infiltration rate is lost by surface runoff. The water acceptance rate of a soil may be seriously reduced if precipitation is in the form of large drops. These can damage the structure of the soil surface, its tilth, causing the crumbs to slake and coalesce into a dense saturated layer through which water can penetrate only slowly; the result is again water wastage by runoff. Methods of countering such wastage are mentioned in chapter 9.

EVAPORATION

Water evaporates into the air from any wet surface, be it the liquid water of lakes, streams and the sea, wet soil or foliage, or the moist surfaces of the cells of the spongy parenchyma in leaves (see chapter 5). Water can also sublime or pass directly from the solid state on the surface of ice and snow into the vapour state in the atmosphere. The rate of evaporation is governed by the incident radiant energy and the temperature, humidity and motion of the air immediately above the evaporating surface (see chapter 8). The important point in the present discussion is that transpiration from plants is a passive evaporation process subject to the same constraints as evaporation from nonliving surfaces. Indeed it is reasonable to include transpiration with all these other modes of water loss in the general term 'evaporation'. The term 'evapo-transpiration' seems superfluous.

DEW

In early morning following a clear cool night considerable quantities of liquid water may be found on exposed surfaces which have been subject to heat loss by radiation during the night; in the UK heavy dewfall is characteristic of autumn weather. Substantial dewfall occurs in certain deserts where intense back radiation during the very clear nights cools horizontal surfaces well below the dewpoint, the temperature at which the air is saturated by its current moisture content, and so condensation ensues.

Dew is derived mainly from water evaporated from the soil during the early part of the night and subsequently condensed onto surfaces cooled by radiation. Thus it does not constitute a net gain in the sense that normal precipitation increases the water content of the plant-soil system. On the other hand the presence of dew on leaves temporarily reduces their transpiration rate and thus reduces their water demand on the soil. Eventually the dew itself evaporates and so constitutes a net loss to the system.

DRAINAGE

As will be described in chapter 3 soils can hold a characteristic amount of water against free drainage and when this amount has been reached any further water falling upon the surface causes displacement of an equivalent amount downwards, constituting the drainage. Such drainage water moves out of reach of the roots and so must be regarded as lost to the immediate plant-soil system; also lost with the water is soluble fertiliser leached away from the root zone.

In the UK drainage takes place mainly during the winter months and its amount is predictable with some accuracy. Tables have been produced to indicate for any district the likely date of return of the soil to field capacity (see page 42) as a result of rainfall accumulation exceeding evaporation and transpiration losses. Other tables indicate when spring evaporation begins to exceed rainfall and from these and the intervening rainfall amounts the likely excess of rain over evaporation, that is the drainage amount, can be estimated for a variety of weather patterns. In central England the average winter drainage totals about 170 mm (7 in).

THE WATER BALANCE

The relationship between precipitation (water input), evaporation, transpiration and drainage (water output) is shown in figure 1.3 which gives values for the different terms measured in a year of average weather in central England. Of the year's total precipitation about half is transpired through plants, about one fifth is wasted in summer by evaporation from the wet soil surface between the plants and about one third is wasted during winter by drainage through the soil.

WATER NEED MAPS

It is evident that the current water need of a horticultural holding will vary at different times during the year according to the crops then growing, the

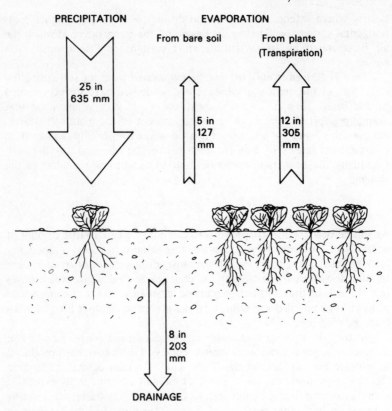

Figure 1.3 Relationship between average annual precipitation, evaporation and drainage in central England.

rainfall and the evaporation rate. Maps similar to isohyet maps enable past weather data to be used to predict irrigation requirements. Figure 1.4 shows how much irrigation would be needed in the driest of twenty years to ensure that a soil moisture deficit of 75 mm (3 in) was never exceeded during April, May and June. In practice it is more reasonable to budget for meeting the full irrigation need in only fifteen years out of twenty, accepting a degree of unfulfilled requirement in the five driest years.

Figure 1.5 shows the number of years in twenty in which some irrigation would be needed to ensure that the soil moisture deficit did not exceed 75 mm (3 in) during June or July.

The maps shown are examples taken from a comprehensive atlas which covers individual months and groups of months throughout the UK growing season and is used when planning irrigation schemes to estimate the quantities of water which may be required in each month at that particular location.

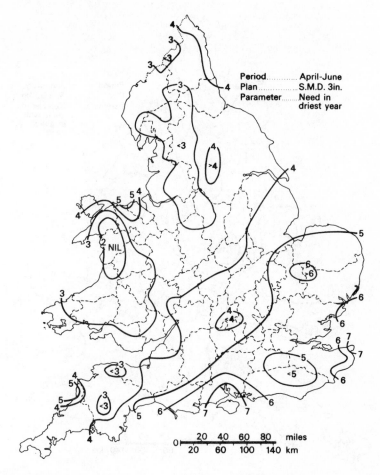

Figure 1.4 Inches of irrigation water needed to prevent the soil moisture deficit (SMD) exceeding 3 in (75 mm) from April to June in the driest year in 20. Reproduced from *Atlas of Irrigation Need 1967* by premission of H.M. Stationery Office.

MEASURING THE WATER BALANCE

Weather recording

From the agricultural and horticultural viewpoint one of the most important weather parameters is the evaporative power of the environment. This may be *measured* using an evaporation tank, evaporimeter or transpirometer (see pages 16 *et seq.*) or *estimated* from meteorological data. The main function of agrometeorological stations is to provide daily records of immediately past weather, one use of which is

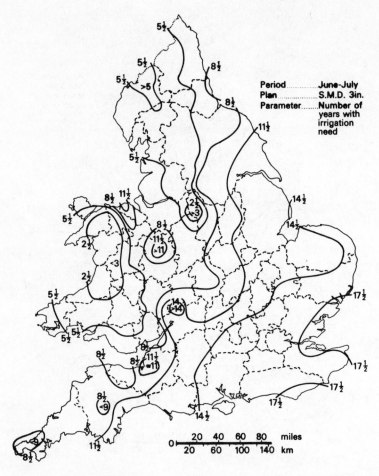

Figure 1.5 Number of years in 20 when irrigation would be needed to prevent soil moisture deficit exceeding 3 in (75 mm) during June and July. Reproduced from *Atlas of Irrigation Need 1967* by permission of H.M. Stationery Office.

to determine how much water has been lost from the plant/soil system and hence the possible irrigation need. In contrast the instruments at synoptic weather stations are read more frequently, usually every four hours for updating large-area charts for forecasting purposes.

Essential instruments at an agrometeorological station include a raingauge, sunshine recorder, maximum and minimum thermometers, wet and dry bulb thermometers, an anemometer, a wind direction vane and earth thermometers at depths ranging from the surface down to one metre. A special thermometer set immediately above short grass, or better, a concrete paving slab, records the occurrence of radiation ('ground') frosts.

A desirable additional instrument is the solarimeter, a thermopile which produces a voltage proportional to solar radiation falling upon it; this operates a recorder and gives an integrated sum of the energy which has fallen upon the site, from which a highly accurate estimate of evaporation can be made (see page 102).

Precipitation measurement

Rainfall is expressed as the depth to which a horizontal surface would be covered uniformly by the whole of the water or melted snow or hail which has fallen upon it.

Instruments for measuring rainfall comprise a collecting funnel of known area and a receiver. The volume of water collected may be measured manually or there may be automatic means for recording quantity, time and rate of precipitation (figure 1.6). A raingauge must incorporate means for minimising evaporation of the collected water before it is measured. Snow accumulated in the funnel is melted by addition of a known volume of warm water which is subsequently subtracted from the record.

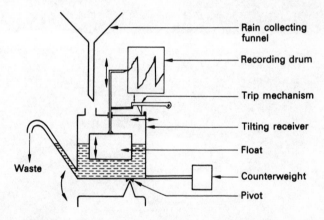

Figure 1.6 Principle of Dyne's tilting siphon recording raingauge; rain accumulates in the receiver, causing the float to rise and lift the pen thus recording the quantity and time of precipitation on the rotating drum. At the upper limit of its travel the float operates a trigger mechanism which allows the full receiver to tilt and so start the siphon. When the receiver has emptied the counterweight resets the mechanism.

Many countries have developed individual raingauge designs and have collected continuous records with these assorted gauges for long periods. Some of these gauges have inherent faults which result in collection errors but most authorities would be unwilling to abandon their old-established gauges in favour of an international standard gauge because it is arguable that continuity of even moderately faulty records made with the same

Figure 1.7 Ground level raingauges with two different methods of reducing insplashing.

Above — set in a domestic coconut fibre mat.

Below — set in a 2 m diameter pit covered with hexagon mesh.

pattern of instrument over long periods is locally more useful than the ability to compare accurate contemporary records between different countries.

In steeply sloping country it is theoretically desirable to express precipitation amount not on the basis of depth of a hypothetical horizontal layer comprising the plan view of the land, but on the depth to which a plane parallel to the hillside would be covered. Special raingauges with inclined funnels have been used in such circumstances.

Large errors can result from siting a gauge in the rain 'shadow' of a building or bush; there should be no object nearer to the gauge than twice the height of the obstruction. The collecting funnel should be near to the soil level to avoid errors in collection caused by wind eddying round the support or the gauge itself. The risk of rain splashing in from the soil surface can be minimised by siting the gauge over vegetation instead of bare soil and the standard United Kingdom gauge is set with its rim 0.3 m (12 in) above short grass. This is a compromise and such a gauge still suffers collection loss resulting from wind eddies. These eddies may be reduced by placing a 2 m diameter turf wall around the gauge. A more effective solution is to sink the gauge in a 2 m diameter pit so that its rim is at the original ground level and to cover the pit with a non-splash surface such as wire mesh or louvres like the slats of a venetian blind, sloping away from the gauge. Rain catch in ground level gauges of this kind approximates closely to the amount of precipitation actually falling upon the ground and may be 12 per cent more than the standard gauge catch (figure 1.7).

The horticulturist who wishes to carry out properly ordered irrigation must have ready access to locally applicable rainfall measurements, or he must install his own simple gauge. For irrigation purposes elaborate precautions against insplash and wind eddies are not necessary but it is essential to site the gauge correctly as described above.

Dewfall measurement

Dew is difficult to measure and the validity of any measurement is open to question because dewfall is closely related to the nature of the material on which it is being deposited, including the heat conductivity, specific heat and the radiation properties of the surface which depend on colour and smoothness. The Duvdevani dew gauge consists of a standard block of polished hardwood exposed horizontally; dewfall is assessed by comparing the appearance of the deposit with standard photographs of known deposits.

A better but more expensive instrument is the surface wetness gauge (figure 1.8) which consists of a white expanded polystyrene ball carried on one arm of a balance. Water deposition on the ball causes weight changes which are recorded continuously on a moving chart to give both time and quantity of dewfall. This equipment has a special use for deciding whether foliage is sufficiently wet for fungus spore germination and hence whether fungicide spraying should be carried out.

To ensure only dew is measured, the gauge must be sheltered from rainfall.

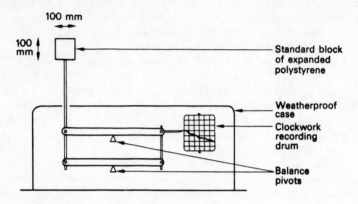

Figure 1.8   Principle of a recording surface wetness gauge.

Evaporation measurement

Evaporation is usually expressed as mm or in of water which would have been lost from an open fresh water surface of infinite area and depth. Evaporation is, of course, negative precipitation but the negative sign is conventionally omitted; care is needed in calculations involving both rainfall and evaporation.

Open water evaporation may be measured directly by observing depth changes in a suitably exposed tank or measuring the volume which must be added from time to time to counteract depth change, in each case allowing for any addition ('negative evaporation' or 'condensation') from rainfall.

Like raingauges evaporation tanks come in a variety of shapes and sizes; some are buried so that the water surface is level with the surrounding soil, some are insulated, some are read manually and some have automatic depth reinstatement and recording devices. Evaporation from all such tanks is highly susceptible to the influence of nearby trees or buildings and the nature of the surrounding surface. Siting to obtain valid readings is a matter of some difficulty and it is usually accepted that the evaporative potential of the environment is better estimated from meteorological observations than measured directly. Nevertheless with care in siting, maintenance and operation, evaporation tanks can be made to yield meaningful results. Figure 1.9 shows the 1.8 m (6 ft) square sunken UK pattern and the 1 m diameter raised US Class A pan. The standard Russian tank is a 20 m square pond. Figure 1.10 shows a simple easily made water level measure.

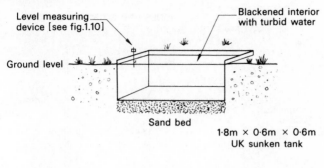

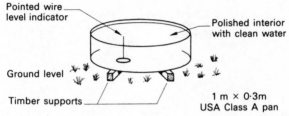

Figure 1.9 UK sunken evaporation tank (above) and USA Class A evaporation pan (below).

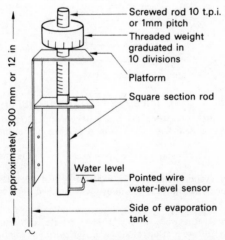

Figure 1.10 Winter and Moore's gauge (1968) for measuring evaporation tank water level. The vertical rod is screwed at 1 mm pitch or at 10 threads per inch (¾ in Whitworth). One revolution of the internally-threaded weight thus raises the wire sensor either 1 mm or 0.1 in; its position can be read to 0.1 revolution equivalent to 0.1 mm or 0.01 in vertical change in water level. In use, the weight, resting on the platform, is rotated until the point of the wire sensor just cuts the water surface. Differences between successive readings adjusted for precipitation indicate evaporation.

Winter, E. J., and Moore, R. A. (1968). A new pattern hookgauge for evaporation tanks. *Weather*, **23**, 2, 82.

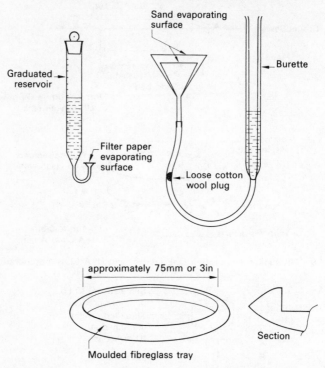

PICHÉ EVAPORIMETER

JONES AND ROTHWELL'S
GLASSHOUSE EVAPORIMETER

Sand evaporating
surface

Burette

Graduated
reservoir

Filter paper
evaporating
surface

Loose cotton
wool plug

approximately 75mm or 3in

Section

Moulded fibreglass tray

HUDSON'S FIELD EVAPORIMETER

Figure 1.11   The Piché evaporimeter is a water-filled graduated reservoir having a small exit U—tube closed with a horizontal filter paper evaporating surface of standard area.

In Jones and Rothwell's glasshouse evaporimeter (1965) the evaporating surface is wet sand.

Hudson's field evaporimeter (1963) is a water-filled fibreglass tray of aerofoil section and supported in the foliage canopy. It is weighed periodically to determine water loss.

Jones, D. A., and Rothwell, J. B. (1965). Private communication. Fairfield Experimental Horticulture Station, Ministry of Agriculture, Fisheries and Food.

Hudson, J. P. (1963). Variations in evaporation rates in Gezira cotton fields. *Emp. Cotton Growing Rev.*, **40**, 253—61.

Evaporation tanks may be used to measure the current deficit of rainfall below evaporation when assessing irrigation need (see chapter 8). For this purpose rain is *not* subtracted from the water level in the tank. Good results, suitable for use in horticulture, have been obtained under widely differing conditions in Kenya, Israel and the UK.

The evaporative power of the environment can also be measured with a variety of smaller instruments (figure 1.11). The Piché evaporimeter and Jones and Rothwell's instrument designed for use in commercial glasshouses have means for measuring the volume of water expended in keeping a paper or sand surface wet. The Hudson tray has a pool of water exposed in a standard container from which loss is measured periodically by weighing. For agricultural use combined evaporimeters and raingauges have been designed in which input is automatically set against output to give a direct indication of the current soil moisture deficit or surplus. (see figure 9.2, page 110).

For reasons described in chapter 8 the evaporative power of the environment regulates the quantity of water removed from the plant-soil system and hence the amount which could be replaced without overfilling the soil reservoir. The evaporimeter reading is thus a maximum; it can exceed the optimum amount of irrigation which depends upon soil, plant species and stage of growth and the kind of produce required. All these are discussed later.

The most straightforward way to relate an instrument reading to irrigation need is to calibrate the device empirically for the particular circumstances in which it is to be used. Irrigation water should be added cautiously to the soil and its progress downwards should be followed by frequent augering. A record is required of the amount of water or the duration of operation of the irrigation system needed to rewet the soil to the full rooting depth of the plants, without causing waterlogging or drainage. Repetition of this process for different readings of the evaporimeters or other instruments will enable a simple graph to be built up from which the quantity of irrigation required to rewet the soil at any instrument reading can be ascertained. This procedure cannot be expected to yield highly accurate results but will be adequate for the unavoidably variable commercial growing conditions. The effects of environment variability can be minimised by using the average reading derived from a number of instruments at representative locations throughout the glasshouse or field.

Lysimeters

Evaporation from the plant/soil system can be measured by repeatedly weighing a block of soil together with the plants growing in it, assuming that weight changes are the result of changes in total water content and neglecting the comparatively minute changes due to respiration and photosynthesis. Figure 1.12 shows examples of both large and small weighable lysimeters. A common fault in lysimeters is that the soil block is necessarily enclosed and thus isolated from the surrounding soil and subsoil; suction devices are sometimes inserted under the enclosed soil to counteract the effects of isolation on the water potential (see page 38). Confinement of the soil also restricts the possible root range of the plants

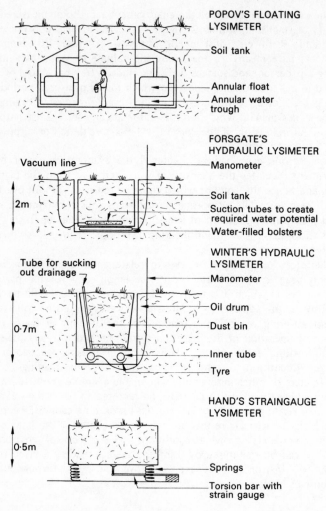

Figure 1.12 Operating principles of novel lysimeters; other instruments use conventional weighing machines.

Popov's lysimeter (1959) is supported on airfilled floats in an annular trough; changes in freeboard indicate weight change.

Forsgate's lysimeter (1965) rests on a metal water-filled bolster, the pressure inside which is related to the weight and is measured on a manometer.

Winter's lysimeter (1963) uses everyday materials; the plastic bin (soil tank) rests on a water-filled automobile inner tube cradled in half of the tyre cover; the air valve is removed and a manometer tube attached to the connector.

Hand's lysimeter (1968); most of the weight is taken on coil springs while the small remainder is taken by four torsion bars. Strain gauges sense the deformation of the bars and provide a continuous electrical signal indicating the weight.

Forsgate, J. A., Hosegood, P. H. and McCulloch, J. S. G. (1965). Design and installation of a semi-enclosed hydraulic lysimeter. *Agr. Meteorol.* 2, 43—52.

Hand, D. W. (1968). An electrically-weighed lysimeter based on the use of strain gauges. *Agr. Meterol.* 5, 269—282.

Popov, O. V. (1959). Lysimeters and hydraulic soil evaporimeters. *Publ. Assoc. int. hydrol. Sci.* No. 49, 26—37.

Winter, E. J. (1963). A new type of lysimeter. *J. hort. Sci.* 38, 160—8.

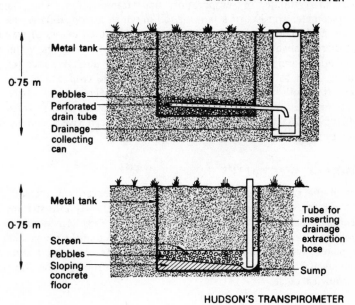

GARNIER'S TRANSPIROMETER

Metal tank

0·75 m

Pebbles
Perforated drain tube
Drainage collecting can

Metal tank

0·75 m

Screen
Pebbles
Sloping concrete floor

Tube for inserting drainage extraction hose

Sump

HUDSON'S TRANSPIROMETER

Figure 1.13   Typical transpirometers or drainage lysimeters.

Hudson, J. P. (1968). Lysimeters and weighable containers in greenhouse experimentation. *Acta Hort.*, 7, 104—14.

Garnier, B. J. (1952). A simple apparatus for measuring potential evapotranspiration. *Nature, Lond.*, 170, 286—7.

under investigation. When setting up a lysimeter it is technically much simpler and cheaper to fill it with excavated soil instead of confining a large undisturbed monolith, although the latter has been done. Even with careful attention to replacing the soil horizons in their correct order and packing to the original density the physical and biological properties of the soil in a refilled lysimeter inevitably differ from those in undisturbed soil. Hence it is preferable to compare the effects of different treatments all applied in similar lysimeters instead of attempting to relate lysimeter observations to those made in nearby unconfined soil.

Drainage measurement

A crude estimate of drainage from horticultural land may be made by observing the outfall from land drains. Continuous recording instruments have been developed for this purpose. Drain outfall does not include drainage past the collecting tile pipes and mole cavities into the subsoil. Drainage lysimeters produce drainage water and hence give results only when the soil contains water in excess of field capacity (see page 42). So-called transpirometers (figure 1.13) are drainage lysimeters used also to yield an estimate of evaporation and transpiration. The Garnier transpirometer consists of a tank of soil in which a crop, usually grass, is grown. Each day the tank is irrigated with a measured excess of water so that there is always some drainage. The difference between the volume of water added and that collected as drainage, with due allowance for any rain, is taken to be the amount transpired by the crop and evaporated from the soil. Because drainage proceeds over several days the indeterminate amount of storage in the soil causes errors which are difficult to assess. Nevertheless this instrument can give a comparative guide to the water balance in different localities.

SUMMARY OF CHAPTER 1

Part of the rain falling on the land is stored temporarily in the soil; part runs off the surface into ditches; part drains shallowly into streams and eventually reaches the sea; part drains deeper into long-term storage in the aquifers. Utilising energy from the sun, water stored in the soil is taken up by plants and evaporated or transpired into the atmosphere where it rejoins water evaporated from the soil surface and from the sea. This is the hydrological cycle.

CHAPTER 2

WATER SUPPLIES FOR HORTICULTURE

Normal crop plants obtain most of their water needs through their root systems dispersed in the soil; most plants can also take up liquid water directly through the surface of their leaves as can be observed by immersing cut, wilted, foliage in water but this mode of uptake is of minor importance in the growing plant.

The depth of soil exploited by root systems varies according to the kind of plant, the type of soil and the presence or absence of a water table. Common ephemeral crop plants such as cauliflowers, peas and lettuce have root systems which are most effective in the top metre of soil; a grass sward exploits a similar depth but the roots of certain plants such as lucerne can range more than 6 m deep. Plants adapted to arid conditions, such as cacti and succulents, have deep ranging widely dispersed root systems as do some of the more successful temperate zone weeds. As might be expected perennial fruit trees usually have deeper root systems than ephemeral plants but the actual depth tapped varies with the kind of soil and especially upon the presence of air as determined by the drainage conditions. Roots of tea under favourable conditions in light well drained soil have been found 10 m deep, but on sodden peat soil the entire root system is confined to the few centimetres above the water table where the peat does contain some air.

Most of the water exploited by crop plants is derived from precipitation entering the soil through its surface. A comparatively small amount of water rises into the root zone from lower layers as a result of capillary action but the rate of this movement is slow. Upward capillary movement is the main source for potted plants in one commercially-used automatic watering system in which the plant containers rest on a wet sand bed whose supply comes from a water table artificially maintained a few centimetres below its surface (figure 9.6, page 126).

Lateral movement of water by mass flow in the voids between the soil crumbs takes place at about the same rate as downward movement in saturated soil and forms the major mode of transport to the roots in furrow-irrigated beds.

(Movement of water in soil is dealt with more fully in chapter 4).

Except in lands with cool moist summers such as the most northerly of temperate zones, and in tropical rain forests, some excess of evaporation over precipitation during the growing season is virtually universal, and if it is accepted that freedom from moisture stress is a prerequisite of maximum growth then it follows that supplementary watering will increase growth in most of the cropped areas of the world, with the obvious exception of crops such as rice and watercress which are grown under swamp conditions. It must be emphasised that induction of maximum growth by elimination of water stress is by no means always economically sound and this point will be enlarged upon in chapter 9. We are here remarking that supplementary watering will increase the growth of most normal crop plants and that this supplementary water is exploited by plants mainly through their root systems which take it up from the soil. Thus the farmer must try to ensure that his soil is adequately supplied with water, supplementing rain when economically practicable by artificial irrigation of some kind.

SOURCES OF WATER; PUMPING MACHINERY

Water supplies for irrigation may be obtained from ponds, springs, drains, lakes, streams and rivers, from shallow wells or deep bores, or for comparatively small installations, from the public supply mains. In some circumstances irrigation water may be drawn from brackish estuaries. Usually pumping is necessary and equipment used includes primitive but ingenious man-powered or animal operated lifts, bucket chain devices and water wheels, reciprocating lift and force pumps, air-lift pumps and centrifugal pumps driven by wind, internal combustion engines or electric motors.

Most modern irrigation installations use centrifugal pumps powered by internal combustion engines or electric motors. The latter have the advantage of ease of control and are readily adaptable to automation. 'Automatic' stopping of small internal combustion engines is sometimes arranged by placing only sufficient fuel in the tank to pump the required quantity of water. Pumps may be driven from a tractor power takeoff but it is uneconomical to use a sophisticated engine designed to have a wide speed range, and mounted on an expensive propulsion unit with complex and expensive ancillary devices merely to provide constant-speed rotary power; furthermore the heavy continuous load imposed by a centrifugal water pump can cause excessive engine wear. In Russia self-propelled irrigators have been developed to travel slowly alongside water channels drawing up water through a trailing suction hose and spraying it over adjacent crops.

ABSTRACTION POINTS

The complexity of the works on the bank of a lake or stream depends upon whether there may be fluctuations in water level, floating debris, algal or similar pollution of the water, and the required rate of abstraction. In its simplest form the abstraction apparatus consists merely of a non-collapsible suction pipe trailing down the bank and usually terminating in a non-return valve to retain priming water in the pump when it is not operating; this elementary arrangement is satisfactory only on a very small scale. It is better to suspend the intake clear of the bottom using a float; floating intakes are suitable for a wide range of equipment. Large fixed installations usually require purpose-designed concrete works to support the intake pipes, grids, filters, sluices, pumps, power units, meters, delivery manifolds and control valves.

CROSS-STREAM DAMS AND OFF-STREAM POUNDS

Difficulties consequent upon fluctuation in water level or insufficient stream flow to meet the required rate of abstraction may be overcome by damming a watercourse to form an artificial on-stream pound, or by constructing a leat or water channel to supply an excavated off-stream pound (figure 2.1). Sometimes local conditions permit water to percolate sufficiently rapidly into an isolated abstraction well sited near the stream bank. Alternatively a reservoir near the stream and preferably above its normal level may be fed by pumping.

With all impounding schemes it is of paramount importance to provide an ample overflow channel to prevent build-up of excessive and dangerous waterlevel behind the dam in time of abnormal stream flow.

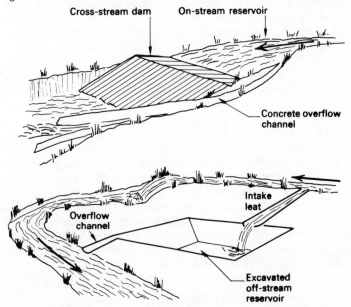

Figure 2.1 On-stream and off-stream reservoirs; alternatively an off-stream reservoir may be above stream-level and be fed by pumping.

ARTIFICIAL LAKES AND RESERVOIRS

Until comparatively recently the feasibility of building an artificial lake depended upon the presence of natural impermeable strata which would retain the water in the excavation or upstream of a dam. The alternative of lining with clay or concrete was too expensive for all but the smallest reservoirs. Flexible lining materials are now available which can be used to waterproof permeable sites. Lining sheets may be of polyethylene (cheap, but not easy to join except by heat-welding, and liable to puncture), polyvinyl chloride or PVC (more expensive, but tough and capable of being joined by cold adhesive) or butyl rubber (about half the cost of reinforced concrete, easy to join with cold adhesive, highly resistant to sunlight, abrasion and puncture and virtually everlasting.) Other materials for waterproofing include bituminous felt and bitumen or pitch-soaked straw matting. It is also possible to make artificial impermeable horizons in light soils or sands by injection with materials which will react to form water repellent silicone compounds.

WELLS AND BOREHOLES

Excavated surface wells have been used to obtain irrigation water since the dawn of history but their success depends upon the presence of a water table near enough to the surface to be exploited by a lift pump (maximum practicable suction lift about 8 m) or one of the many ingenious hauled-bucket devices common throughout the tropics, sometimes comprising a number of lifts in tandem to raise water from great depths.

Tube wells consist of smallbore (less than 100 mm diameter) pipes sunk into water-bearing strata; a tube well can be operated by suction pump only if the water rises by artesian pressure to within 8 m of the surface.

Bore holes, 0.3 m or more in diameter, may be driven unlined through stable rock formations but must be lined with rigid pipes when passing through soft material such as clay or sand. Usually the water is extracted by means of a submersible pump suspended on the delivery pipe which itself hangs in the bore, together with the electricity supply cables. The only limit then set on the depth from which the water can be raised is the power of the pump itself. The motor may be at the surface driving the submerged pump through a vertical shaft inside the delivery pipe. One method of avoiding the need for submerged machinery in the borehole is to raise the water by entraining it in compressed air pumped down an inner pipe and released at the well bottom.

PUBLIC WATER SUPPLIES

When the public main is tapped for irrigation supplies the local authority usually insists on the installation of a holding tank large enough to meet the irrigation requirements for at least twenty-four hours; this is to avoid undesirable pressure reduction in the main arising from the heavy operating demand of most irrigation equipment.

LAND DRAINS

The use of land drains to provide irrigation water supplies has not been widely exploited. Reference to figure 1.3 shows that even in a land with

Figure 2.2   Above − 23 000 m³ reservoir; in foreground, irrigated strawberries.
Below − The inflow from tile drains under 100 hectares of land; this reservoir is built on pervious soil and rendered watertight with a butyl rubber lining.

modest rainfall such as the UK, receiving only about 200 mm during the winter months, 175 mm of this can be lost by drainage. Conserving only a fraction of this in a suitable farm reservoir would meet a significant part of the following summer's irrigation requirements.

In a typical case (figure 2.2) ample water was collected from the land drains under 100 hectares (250 acres) to fill a 23 000 m³ (5 million gallon) reservoir in three winter months and this represented only about one-sixth of the water which had fallen upon the soil, leaving five-sixths to replenish the aquifers and meet the needs of other consumers.

UNDERGROUND RECHARGE

Normally waterbearing strata or aquifers are replenished by vertical percolation through permeable strata above them or by horizontal percolation through sloping permeable strata, themselves replenished at the location where they break the earth's surface (figure 2.3). Intense

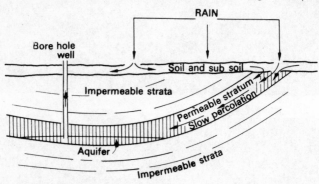

Figure 2.3   Replenishment of a deep aquifer from a distant point where it breaks the earth's surface.

exploitation of an aquifer through a multiplicity of boreholes can denude it at a rate faster than it is naturally replenished; such a situation is especially serious where the aquifer consists of a saucer-shaped formation perched above a similarly dished impermeable stratum. It may be feasible to replenish an aquifer when there is excess water on the surface, such as during winter flooding, by pumping water down suitable boreholes. Where the geological formation happens to be favourable it is possible to recover a worthwhile percentage of the water thus stored. It is essential to introduce only pure water in this manner, for fear of irrevocably polluting the aquifer.

An alternative system has been developed in which polluted water is distributed over waste land either with irrigation equipment, or in lagoons. The water percolates first through the soil and then through permeable strata beneath and much of the pollutant is left behind as in a vast filter.

Water thus reaching the deep aquifer is comparatively pure and can be extracted for use. The length of time for which such a system is viable obviously depends on the nature of the pollutants. Suspended solid particles are retained in the surface layers of the soil or lagoons whence the sludge can be removed for disposal; some organic pollutants can be decomposed by the soil organisms, but dissolved pollutants will be distributed throughout the permeable system where it is claimed that adsorption and dilution by purer water coming in from other sources renders them harmless.

ESTUARINE BARRAGES

In the UK feasibility studies have been conducted to ascertain the practicability of converting large coastal inlets such as the Wash, Morecambe Bay, the Severn and even the Thames estuary into great freshwater lakes of the type engineered successfully in Holland. To do this the inlet must be isolated from the sea by a barrage across its mouth; fresh water continues to be discharged by rivers into the enclosed lake whose level is constrained by pumping or draining the surplus into the sea. Thus its salinity is gradually lowered until after a period which could be of the order of ten years, the water is fresh enough to use. Thereafter abstraction must be matched to the river discharge into the lake to maintain flow through non-return sluices into the sea and also to maintain an underground positive hydrostatic pressure, so permanently keeping out the sea water.

It has been suggested that such schemes would assure the water supplies of the UK for the forseeable future, but even if enough freshwater lakes were established around the coastline the major problem of water distribution would still remain. This is of comparatively straightforward solution for domestic supplies in densely populated areas, but the distribution network for supplying individual farms at a distance from the main water flumes would be extremely costly.

THE SEA AS A POSSIBLE SOURCE OF IRRIGATION WATER

Desalination of seawater is technologically feasible by several different methods. Atomic energy has been suggested as a source of heat for distillation but the cost will probably exceed that of other processes and this system is unlikely to be adopted except possibly in arid countries where there is no other practicable source.

In the process called reverse osmosis water is pumped at very high pressure through a semi-permeable membrane whose pores are too small to allow even the ionised solutes in the water to pass. Though expensive in power consumption the cost of the equipment is much less than that utilising atomic heat. Nevertheless the method is unlikely to be practicable for producing the large volumes of water needed for irrigation.

In hot sunny climates solar distillation is feasible. Saline water is held in a black trough covered by inclined sheets of glass. Glass is transparent to longwave radiation with only a small concurrent temperature rise and the heat admitted is absorbed by the black walls of the trough and heats them together with the contained water; the air above the water becomes saturated with vapour which condenses on the underside of the glass because this is cooler than the enclosed atmosphere. The distillate runs down into collecting gutters. The equipment cost is small and running costs almost nil but the output rate is low; the system is suitable for drinking water production, but for irrigation only on a very small scale.

Although undiluted sea water can be utilised by specialised maritime plants (halophytes) its salt concentration is too high for normal crop plants, but the brackish water of estuaries has been used successfully for irrigation. The salt burden that can be tolerated by various plants is discussed on page 32.

WATER QUALITY

Nearly half of the water used for irrigation in the United Kingdom comes from surface sources, that is sources other than deep boreholes. These sources, rivers, lakes and surface wells are all *liable* to pollution from untreated farm effluents, factory discharges and imperfectly treated effluent from sewage works overloaded in time of heavy rain. In 1967 about 7% of the total length of all UK rivers was severely polluted.

So-called 'organic irrigation' in which the effluent from intensive cattle or poultry enterprises is sprayed on farmland is to be regarded as a means of disposing of embarrassing sewage rather than as a means of soil fertilisation; the comparatively trivial nutrient content of this material could be more economically supplied as inorganic fertiliser and the action of the sludge on the physical conditions of the soil is quite different from that of farmyard manure made from straw. The use of sludge on open fields and 'manure water' in glasshouses is obviously undesirable for crops which are to be eaten raw, and where water contaminated with human or animal excreta is used for irrigation this should be done by furrow or subsoil watering and not by spraying, to keep pathogens off the foliage. Complete sterilisation of the produce is almost impossible except by cooking and even if only a few bacteria remain on the leaves of lettuce, for example, they can multiply rapidly to dangerous concentrations in the warm humid atmosphere of a shop. Disease outbreaks have been traced to the presence of the bacillus *Salmonella* on celery, watercress, water melon and other fruits.

For produce to be eaten raw, the best source of irrigation water is a deep borehole. Where surface sources are used care must be taken in choosing a draw-off point proven to be free from contamination, to inspect frequently to ensure that it remains so and to avoid introducing untreated farm effluent upstream of the intake. Equipment is available for sterilising large volumes of water but the procedure is expensive.

DISSOLVED SALTS

The salt burden of a water source may be increased by excessive upstream irrigation of crops given heavy applications of fertiliser, by evaporation from reservoirs, by recycling and reusing water and by direct pollution from factory wastes and dumps of materials such as pulverised fuel ash, slag and coal waste. Excess salinity is harmful to crops because of osmotic stress in the soil water and also because of the toxicity of the salts themselves. In addition to the common metallic ions, elements such as boron, arsenic and selenium and the heavy metals may be present in toxic concentrations.

Crops vary in their sensitivity to toxic elements and soils vary in their ability to occlude or release harmful materials.

ACCUMULATION OF SALTS IN THE SURFACE SOIL

Water normally moves downwards through the soil, but under high evaporative conditions there is slow upward movement by capillarity;

Table 2.1

Tolerance of typical crops to concentration of chloride ion in the soil when at field capacity

Chloride concentration g Cl^-/l	Crops which suffer 10 per cent yield decrease				Sensitivity rating
0.35	strawberry apple plum	tulip daffodil azalea	French bean pea	clover	very sensitive
0.75	raspberry	gladiolus rose	onion carrot lettuce	maize cocksfoot meadow foxtail	sensitive
1.45	grape	chrysan- themum carnation clematis	cauli- flower cabbage potato	wheat oat lucerne ryegrass	moderately tolerant
2.50			red beet asparagus spinach	sugar beet mangold kale barley	tolerant

Data of J. H. Williams (1972). Private communication. Agricultural Development and Advisory Service, Cambridge.

evaporation from the soil surface may then concentrate the solutes to such an extent that the resulting high osmotic pressure may interfere with water uptake and thus reduce plant growth irrespective of whether any particular elements are in phytotoxic concentration.

Table 2.1 shows the relative tolerance to chloride ion of different crop plants; prominent among these are beet and other cultivated plants derived from seashore species. Concentrations as low as 3 mmol/l of chloride (105 ppm Cl) in irrigation water have harmed mature citrus, stone fruits and almonds.

Moderately saline water can be used for irrigation provided that excess is applied at each watering so that there is through drainage and leaching of harmful salts away from the root zone. This is *not* sound irrigation practice where good quality water is available.

In glasshouses the chloride concentration is more harmful than the total salt concentration and where crops are supplied regularly with fertiliser dissolved in the irrigation water chlorine-free fertilisers are commonly used. Each increment of 100 mg/Cl/l of water contained in the soil when at field capacity can depress the yield of glasshouse tomatoes by 2.25 per cent (data of J. H. Williams, *loc. cit.*)

The hazards of irrigating with water containing sodium chloride, such as brackish estuarine water, are associated with both anions and cations. Chloride harms the plants while sodium damages the soil structure especially of soils with high clay content, or silts and silty loams.

ASSESSING WATER SUPPLIES

Measuring stream flow

Surprisingly large quantities of water can be abstracted from apparently insignificant streams provided that they flow continuously. The flow rate of a stream small enough to be dammed can be measured by placing across it a V-notch weir. This is a precisely constructed flat-faced weir having a single right angled notch of sufficient size for all the water to flow over it. Figure 2.4 shows its construction and the relationship between rate of stream discharge and the depth of water immediately above the notch. For flow rates exceeding 225 m³/h (50 000 gal/h) a rectangular notched weir is preferable, while for very large streams concrete weirs of special conformation are used, for example, the Crump weir.

Measuring river flow

At river gauging stations the number of cubic feet of water passing a given point per second (cusecs), or the number of cubic metres per second, is estimated from the current water level or 'stage'. The water level is measured at a fixed point on the river bank, or more accurately in a stillwell connected to the river by an underwater pipe. The gauging system is calibrated by measuring the speed of the water at each point in a

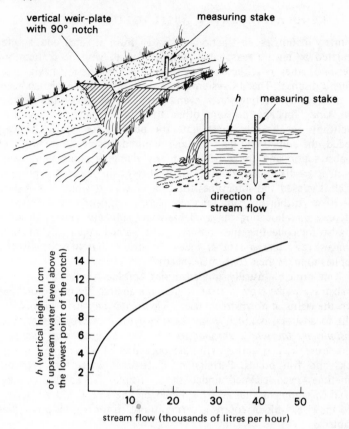

Figure 2.4 Construction and calibration curve for a 90° vee-notch weir. *h* is the undisturbed upstream height of water above the angle of the notch.

representative array in a vertical cross section of the whole river. A propeller-driven water speed indicator is suspended from a cableway spanning the river to take a reading at each required point. From these the average water speed and hence the integrated flow rate can be calculated. This is repeated for many different states of the river flow so that eventually a complete calibration, linking 'stage' directly with flow, is built up.

A very rough estimate of the discharge of a river with a uniform straight channel can be made by measuring the midstream velocity by timing the passage of a float; the average stream velocity is about 0.8 of the midstream velocity, and the cross-sectional area multiplied by this average velocity gives the flow rate.

REGULATING WATER ABSTRACTION

In many countries abstraction of water from streams and aquifers is regulated to ensure reasonable supplies for all who need them and to safeguard other requirements such as those of fisheries, navigation and effluent disposal. The UK system will serve as an example. Here a licence is required for abstracting water, even from a lake wholly on the abstractor's own land, for any purpose other than local domestic consumption. Applicants for licences must state the purpose for which the water is needed, the annual and daily volume required, the peak rate and method of abstraction and the capacity of any pumping equipment. Rates of payment are fixed according to the quality of the water, the purpose for which it is used and sometimes the time of year at which it is abstracted. The River Authorities, one for each major catchment area, are responsible not only for allocating the available water equitably among all interests, but also for collecting and conserving the water in their catchments using barrages, reservoirs and other means to ensure that they have sufficient supplies to meet their consumers' needs.

One principle usually applied during consideration of any application to abstract water from a river is that the abstraction must not interfere with the rights of downstream users. Riparian owners have an ancient legal right to abstract as much water as they wish *provided that they return substantially the whole amount to the river unimpaired in quality.* This right arose in connection with the operation of water mills, navigation locks and fish ponds. Permission to abstract water for irrigation has sometimes been claimed under this principle, the applicant using the mistaken argument that water sprayed on the soil would all drain back into the river; this of course is certainly not so for reasons pointed out in chapter 8.

SUMMARY OF CHAPTER 2

Supplementary water supplies for horticulture come from streams, lakes, surface wells and deep bores, by trapped drainage water and occasionally from public drinking water supplies. It is possible to augment resources by building estuarine barrages and by artificial recharge of aquifers.

Abstraction machinery ranges from primitive but ingenious lift mechanisms to multistage centrifugal pumps driven by electric motors or internal combustion engines.

CHAPTER 3

THE SOIL RESERVOIR

Soil is a complex mixture of inorganic and organic material usually
containing a rich variety of living and dead organisms including bacteria,
fungi, both uni- and multicellular nematodes, molluscs, insects, annelids
and higher animals; soil provides anchorage and support for larger plants
which extract from it their nutrient and water requirements.

The thickness of the soil layer ranges from nil in deserts, steep slopes
and high mountains to hundreds of feet in the ancient peat swamps of
Assam. This distribution indicates the origin of soil which is formed by the
weathering of rocks aided by the growth and decay of plant and animal
material; where the climate will not support life there is no soil. Mineral
soils, as their name implies, consist mainly of rock particles with only a
small proportion of organic matter, whereas peats, muck soils and black
earths consist mainly of organic matter with little mineral admixture.

SOIL SERIES

Soils are classified according to their composition and geological derivation
and each distinct type or series is named usually after the place where it
was first found and scientifically described.

SOIL TEXTURE

The irregularly shaped particles comprising soil vary in size and the particle
size spectrum, or texture, of a soil is the main criterion in classifying it
according to physical characteristics. Table 3.1 shows the size range of
each of the constituent particles, their names and recognised abbreviations.
Table 3.2 shows the mechanical analysis of typical soils, that is the
percentage of each of the different-sized particles which they contain. The
textural class of a soil can be ascertained by reference to the triangular
coordinate diagram, figure 3.1.

SOIL HORIZONS

Soils occur in distinct layers. A horizon is any layer which can be
distinguished visually or texturally from neighbouring layers above and
below. A profile is an assemblage of horizons usually displayed for
examination in the vertical wall of a dug profile pit. The topsoil is the zone

Table 3.1

Size range, names and conventional symbols for the constituent particles in soils;
several different classifications are in current use. In addition to the symbols shown,
L is used to designate loam, defined as a soil containing equal parts of clay, silt and
sand; a sandy loam, silty loam or clay loam contains more of the constituent
indicated

Name	Symbol	Size range in mm		
		International system	*USDA †* *system*	*MIT ‡* *system*
Clay	C	Less than 0.002	Less than 0.002	Less than 0.002
Silt	Z	0.002 − 0.02	0.002 − 0.05	0.002 − 0.006 0.006 − 0.02 0.02 − 0.06
Very fine sand	VFS		0.05 − 0.1	
Fine sand	FS	0.02 − 0.2	0.1 − 0.25	0.06 − 0.2
Medium sand	MS		0.25 − 0.5	0.2 − 0.6
Coarse sand	CS	0.2 − 2.0	0.5 − 1.0	0.6 − 2.0
Very coarse sand	VCS		1.0 − 2.0	
Gravel	G	More than 2.0	2.0 − 75.0	2.0 − 60.0

† United States Department of Agriculture.

‡ Massachusets Institute of Technology; the MIT system was officially adopted by
the Soil Survey of England and Wales in 1972.

of first importance to the horticulturist for it is here that seeds are sown,
plants transplanted and crops established. After establishment the roots
exploit also the subsoil which tends to be less rich in nutrients but at least
as important as the topsoil for supplying water. Beneath the subsoil is the
bedrock. The thickness of the different horizons varies enormously within
and between different soil series.

DRAINAGE

Any or all of the horizons may be freely-draining, that is, water may pass
freely downwards through them, but any may contain more or less
impervious material which can cause local accumulation of water.
Sometimes this may be beneficial and sometimes it may be harmful to

plant growth. It is significant that the would-be crop irrigator is usually advised to see that his land is properly drained before carrying out any watering. Impeded drainage is discussed more fully on page 66.

PORE SPACE

The irregularly shaped particles which comprise soil do not fit closely together; there are inevitably spaces between them and the relative volume of voids to solid material is called the total pore space. The pore space may contain air or water or both; when the whole of the pore space is filled with water the soil is said to be saturated. This condition is not stable and

Table 3.2

Mechanical analysis or particle size distribution of some typical soils

	Percentage by weight of particles †				
Soil texture	*CS 2 – 0.2 mm*	*MS† 0.2 – 0.1 mm*	*FS† 0.1 – 0.02 mm*	*Z 0.02 – 0.002 mm*	*C Less than 0.002 mm*
Coarse sand	82.2	9.6	3.9	1.0	2.7
Sandy loam	49.0	17.8	13.6	4.0	15.0
Loam	1.7	—	51.6	23.3	18.8
Silty loam	20.8	—	24.1	32.7	19.0
Silty clay	2.9	0.6	6.8	48.5	23.2
Clay	31.1	6.1	8.3	10.0	39.5

† According to International System (see table 3.1) except that 'fine sand' has been subdivided into fine and medium fractions.

provided that there is no impedance to drainage, gravity will pull water downwards from a saturated zone towards lower unsaturated zones. The pull of gravity is augmented by the pull of the surface tension which arises in the coating of water surrounding each of the soil particles in zones where the pore spaces are not completely full. The thinner the water film round the particles, the higher is the surface tension and the greater the suction exerted. When a dry layer occurs above a wet layer the surface tension acts in opposition to gravity and may even overcome it so that water moves upwards 'by capillarity'.

SOIL WATER POTENTIALS

The total suction holding water in soil is made up from two components namely matric suction and osmotic suction. These forces are more

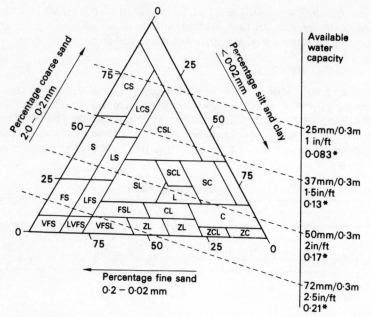

Figure 3.1 Triangular diagram showing particle size composition in terms of percentage clay, silt and sand for typical soil textures, classified according to the International System.

correctly referred to as potentials, but to simplify the explanation of the dynamics of the soil system they will be described in terms of their effects which are suctions.

MATRIC POTENTIAL, OR SUCTION

The matric suction is associated with the physical properties of the matrix of pores and solid material formed by the loosely fitting complex which comprises the fabric of the soil. This suction pervades the whole soil system and tends to equilibrate the moisture status of the soil, subsoil and rock formations beneath, but because the system is being continuously influenced by variables from outside, such as precipitation, evaporation and transpiration, equilibrium is rarely achieved and the whole soil moisture system is in a continual state of flux. Movement of water resulting from this lack of equilibrium is called redistribution.

OSMOTIC POTENTIAL, OR SUCTION

In addition to matric suction the soil water is subject to suction arising from the presence of solutes which create osmotic pressure. Compared

* See page 59.

with matric suction osmotic suction is usually small and may be ignored when measuring or estimating total suction in average conditions. However in special circumstances such as in the surface soil of a seed bed which has received inorganic fertiliser dressing, rapid evaporation between rain or irrigation showers may cause violent fluctuations in soil water content, which in turn affects solution concentration and the osmotic suction to which seeds and seedlings are subjected. Osmotic suction is also significant in saline soils, in soils irrigated with brackish water such as those near estuaries and in some deserts, and in glasshouse culture where a high concentration of fertiliser is normally used.

pF

It will be apparent that total suction must increase as the soil moisture content falls as a result of drainage, evaporation and uptake by roots. Because suction increases very rapidly with drying it is convenient to plot the relationship on a logarithmic scale (figure 3.2) and to describe total suction in terms of its negative logarithm — Schofield's pF. This relationship between suction and moisture content follows a different course according to whether the soil is wetting or drying and this hysteresis is shown in the figure.

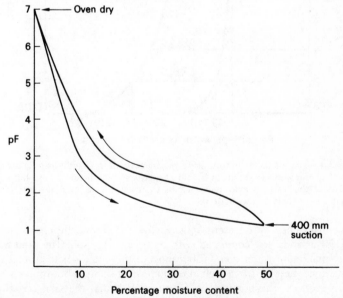

Figure 3.2   Relationship between suction (equivalent to negative water potential) and soil moisture content. Redrawn from Schofield's (1935) original paper defining pF.

Schofield, R. K. (1935). The pF of the water in soil. *Trans. 3rd int. Congr. Soil Sci.*, 37–48.

SOIL MOISTURE CHARACTERISTIC

A similar curve describes matric suction in relation to soil moisture content and is known as Child's moisture characteristic, or characteristic moisture release curve. When, as is often the case, osmotic suction is negligible, the pF curve and the moisture characteristic curve are virtually identical but as pointed out above there are important exceptions to this.

The magnitude of matric suction depends on the size and conformation of the soil particles and so soils with different particle size spectra, or mechanical analyses, yield different pF and characteristic curves. These curves provide convenient ways of describing the moisture

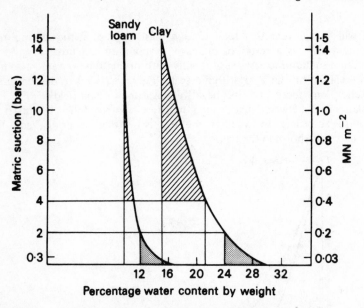

Figure 3.3 The characteristic moisture release curves for a sandy loam and a clay soil; half of the water in the loam is held at matric suction below 2 bars, but in the clay half of the water is held above 4 bars (hatched — water held at high suction, stippled — water held at low suction).

release properties of different soils. Figure 3.3 shows the characteristic curve for a sandy soil compared with that for a clay soil. The sand has a smaller maximum water content but most of the water is held at relatively low suction; the clay has a high maximum water content but much is held at high suction. The horticultural implication is that the sand contains a smaller volume of water very readily available but quickly exhausted, whereas the heavier soil contains more water, held more tightly. Growth is likely to be faster in the sandy soil provided that there is frequent replenishment of the soil water reservoir.

THE LOWER LIMIT OF AVAILABLE WATER ('PERMANENT WILTING POINT)

The forces holding water in soil increase as the moisture content falls (figure 3.3) and so there is a total suction at which water will no longer pass from the soil into roots; transpiration loss then exceeds intake and the foliage wilts. For many soils this happens at about 15 bars (1.5 MN m^{-2}) and it has been customary to refer to the moisture content of soils at 15 bars as 'permanent wilting point' (or 'percentage'). This concept is open to objection because it suggests that all species behave similarly in different soils. This is manifestly not so — see figure 3.4 — where one of the species shown to wilt at different suctions in the two soils is sunflower, a plant often used for the biological determination of permanent wilting point (see page 58). It is therefore better to refer to the lower limit of available water as the 15 bar moisture content, omitting reference to plant behaviour. However, physical determination of the equilibrium moisture content of a soil at 15 bars pressure requires much more complicated apparatus than the biological test. Results of the biological test are acceptable provided that they are clearly defined as the moisture status at which a specified plant, usually sunflower, wilted and did not recover

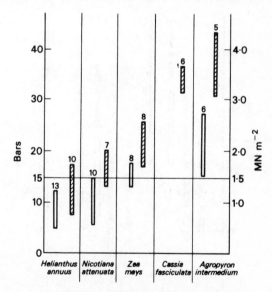

Figure 3.4 Suctions at which five species were found to wilt permanently in a clay loam (open symbols) and a silty clay loam (shaded symbols). Each symbol represents the range of wilting points corresponding to the number of individuals indicated alongside.

Redrawn data of Sykes.

Sykes, D. J. (1969). *Turrialba*, 19, 4.

turgidity even when its foliage was placed in a saturated atmosphere. The significance of this will be discussed in chapter 6. Often, but certainly not always, 'permanent wilting' point determined in this manner approximates to the 15 bar moisture content. As with all biologically determined parameters it is essential to state the precise conditions under which the measurement was made so that these can be reproduced when required. The advantage of the 15 bar moisture content is that it is a precisely defined physical entity, entirely independent of variable living material. Figure 3.5 shows the variable behaviour of sunflower.

THE UPPER LIMIT OF AVAILABLE WATER ('FIELD CAPACITY')

It has been pointed out that saturated soil is in an unstable state; water is pulled down by gravity augmented by the suction exerted by lower unsaturated zones. The pull of gravity is constant but the pull from unsaturated zones depends upon their moisture status; the drier they are, the thinner the film of water round each soil particle and hence the greater the surface tension and suction. The pull of an unsaturated zone also depends upon its vertical depth below the saturated zone because there is a

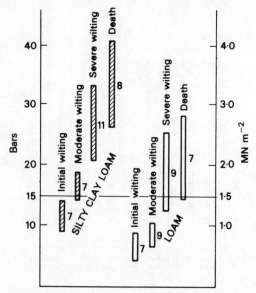

Figure 3.5   Wilting behaviour of sunflower in silty clay loam and in loam.
    Each symbol represents the range of wilting points corresponding to the number of individuals indicated alongside.
    Redrawn data of Sykes.

Sykes, D. J. (1969). *Turrialba*, **19**, 4.

continuous column of water bridging the soil particles and this sets up a simple hydrostatic negative pressure or suction. When this column ends at a water table where there is free water at maximum potential or minimum suction this limitation of its length obviously limits the total suction exerted on the saturated soil above; thus the suction to which a freely draining saturated soil is subject depends on many factors. It is certainly not the same for all soils and all conditions.

The effect of this suction is to drain water out of the saturated zone and replace it with air drawn in from the atmosphere. The rate of drainage depends upon the conductivity of the soil which itself depends upon the water content; the lower the moisture content, the thinner the layer of water round each soil particle and the higher the forces holding it there and impeding movement. Drainage rate is a function of the fourth to the tenth power of water content; that is to say the reduction in drainage rate equals the associated fall in moisture content multiplied by itself at least four times. Thus as drainage proceeds there is a sudden reduction in its rate so that the process appears almost to have ceased; the soil is then said to be at field capacity. Nevertheless there is still a substantial layer of water surrounding the soil particles, conductivity is still finite and so drainage continues albeit very slowly and eventually almost undetectably. In many soils the fall in drainage rate is well marked and field capacity well defined, for example the Newport series in Warwickshire, UK; in others, such as Astley Hall in nearby Nottinghamshire, which is of the same textural class as Newport, drainage continues more or less indefinitely and the term field capacity is meaningless. Although field capacity is a parameter which can often be reproducibly measured, it cannot be defined satisfactorily in physical terms and the only excuse for continuing to use it is that it has a convenient application in field irrigation.

Attempts have been made to locate field capacity on the pF and moisture characteristic scales; the suction of many freely drained soils at field capacity has been found to be about 0.33 bar (33 kN m^{-2}); as pointed out above in the presence of a water table the suction is limited. If the water table is at 2 m the maximum possible suction is 0.2 bar (20 kN m^{-2}). In soils with especially freely available water the suction corresponding to field capacity is no more than 0.1 bar (10 kN m^{-2}). Thus, as with permanent wilting point, when quoting a value for field capacity it is essential to state the conditions under which the measurement was made.

AVAILABLE WATER CAPACITY

It follows from the definitions of field capacity and permanent wilting point that the numerical difference between these two parameters represents the water which plants can abstract from the soil — the available water capacity of the soil, or the capacity of the soil reservoir. When the reservoir is full soil water potential is high and water is readily available for plant uptake. As the soil reservoir water content falls potential also falls, soil suction rises and water uptake by roots becomes increasingly difficult until at permanent wilting point the soil suction exceeds that which can be exerted by the plant system and intake ceases. It has been shown that even beyond permanent wilting point a very small amount of water continues to enter the plant, but this is quite insufficient to support growth.

Field capacity is usually regarded as the upper limit of water available to plants for growth but it may take several days for a soil to drain down to this condition after being saturated. Further rain may fall before the drainage rate is substantially reduced, so that the soil may remain above field capacity for considerable periods. During this time plants have certainly been using water held in the soil in excess of the field capacity figure and this water is usually included in attempts to arrive at accurate

Table 3.3

Available water capacity of different-textured soils, based on their particle size spectra

| Texture* | Percentage moisture content at | | Available water capacity | | |
	(a) Field capacity	(b) Permanent wilting point (unavailable)	in/ft	mm/0.3 m	ratio †
Coarse sand	8	4	1.0	25	0.083
Coarse sandy loam	19	9	1.5	39	0.13
Sandy clay	29	19	1.7	42	0.14
Sand	14	4	1.8	45	0.15
Clay	42	25	2.1	51	0.17
Loam	30	13	2.1	51	0.17
Clay loam	34	28	2.2	54	0.18
Silt loam	39	16	2.3	57	0.19
Loamy very fine sand	25	7	2.6	66	0.22
Very fine sandy loam	28	9	2.6	66	0.22
Very fine sand	20	4	2.7	69	0.23

† To conform with the convention frequently found in publications, available water capacity is given here as a quantity of water per stated depth of soil, but as explained on page 59, available water capacity is better expressed as a dimensionless fraction or ratio which can readily be converted into any convenient units.

estimates of consumptive use, that is, the water actually removed from the soil by the crop.

The soil itself is variable in composition, the individual plants comprising the crop are variable among themselves, the distribution of water by irrigation equipment is far from uniform and even rainfall can vary in amount within a small area, thus for practical horticulture and agriculture attempts at extreme precision in assessing field capacity, permanent wilting point and available water capacity are unnecessary. This is not an excuse for inaccuracy but a reminder that where a parameter is insecurely based, quoting its value to one or more places of decimals is misleading and can give a spurious suggestion of accuracy.

In figure 3.3, page 40, the volume of water held between 0.33 and 15 bar, the available water, can be compared for a clay soil and a sandy soil. Table 3.3 shows available water data for typical soils throughout the textural range. Although the total amount of water held in heavy soils is

Figure 3.6 Cultures of *Helxine soleirolii* in a clay loam (left) and a sand (right) brought to field capacity on the same day and then not watered for one week; there was sufficient available water in the clay loam to maintain turgidity of the plants whereas that in the sand has been exhausted.

high, the amount of *un*available water is also high; in considering the horticultural value of a soil the important feature is not the total waterholding capacity but the available waterholding capacity (figure 3.6). In light soils most of the available water is released at low tensions; it is *readily* available, but quickly exhausted. In heavier soils much of the water is released only at comparatively high tension (figure 3.7). Plants may not grow so fast but the water supply lasts longer.

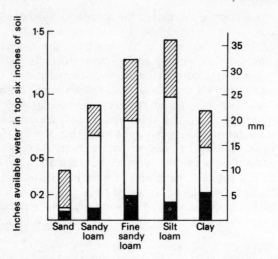

Figure 3.7 Available water capacity of the upper six inches of typical soils; ¾ of the available water in the sand is held at less than 1/3 bar, whereas only ¼ of that in the clay is held at this low tension.

///// held below 1/3 bar

█ held above 8 bar

Data of Salter and Williams (1965) redrawn from figure 2 of their publication.

Salter, P. J. and Williams, J. B. (1965). The influence of texture on the moisture characteristics of soils *J. Soil Sci.* **16**, 310—17.

Available water capacity can be judged roughly from a knowledge of soil texture (figure 3.8); with practice the particle size composition of a soil can be determined by 'hand texturing', that is, by rubbing a moistened sample between the fingers and subjectively deciding the proportion of fine and coarse material it contains. In effect this is a means of classifying the soil. From a knowledge of the classification and thickness of each horizon of a soil it is possible to estimate the total available water capacity in the potential root zone, for example the top 0.8 m (2 ft), by summing the available water capacities of the constituent horizons (figure 3.9).

For some areas of the UK soil maps have been constructed in terms of available water capacity in the top two feet, instead of the usual bases of soil texture or derivation. It is claimed that such maps would aid in planning the future use of land tracts, and the desirability of making supplementary water supplies available.

It is possible to modify soil texture (and hence dependent properties such as available water capacity) by intimately mixing in particles of appropriate size. In the past this has been done by 'marling' (adding clayey material to light soils) but more recently pulverised fuel ash, a waste product of coal-burning electricity generating stations, has been proposed for this purpose, provided that the hazards of possible toxins in this

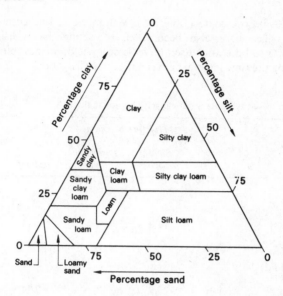

Figure 3.8 Triangular diagram based on Salter and Williams' modified diagram which shows theoretical limits of available water capacity estimated from particle size spectrum (texture) of a sample. High available water capacities are found in soils whose textures lie towards the lower left-hand corner of the triangle.

See also figure 3.1, and table 3.1 for meanings of texture symbols.

Salter, P. J. and Williams, J. B. (1967). The influence of texture on the moisture characteristics of soils. *J. Soil Sci.* 18, 1.

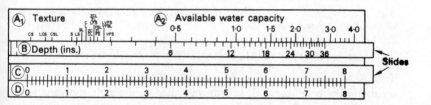

Figure 3.9 Williams' slide rule for totalling available water capacity of a profile from subjective texture assessments.

The 1 mark on slide B is set against the horizon texture on scale A_1; the available water capacity of that horizon (scale A_2) is read opposite its depth on slide B. This is repeated for each horizon of the profile, the measurements being added in turn to a grand total on scale D by moving the zero of slide C the appropriate distances along D.

Williams, J. B. (1966). A device for calculating available water *Expl Agric.* **3**, 159–162.

material can be overcome (table 3.4). Volcanic ash, fine coral sand and pulverised silica have also been used. Increasing the available water capacity of a soil does not itself increase crop yield; the possible value lies in increasing the time interval between necessary irrigations.

Table 3.4
Modification of soil available water capacity by ash additives

	Bulk density	Moisture percentage by weight		Available water capacity	
		Field capacity	Permanent wilting point	ratio †	mm/0.3 m
Natural soil gravelly sandy loam (Wick series)	1.44	16.8	7.5	0.13	40
Same soil with 125 t/ha pulverised fuel ash mixed in top 0.15 m	1.40	23.9	6.6	0.24	73
Same soil with 250 t/ha fluidised combuster ash ‡ mixed in top 0.15 m	1.35	26.2	7.2	0.26	77

† See page 59.

‡ Ash with similar particle size spectrum, but produced in furnaces operated at lower temperature than pulverised fuel furnaces.

Data of Stone, D. A. (1972). Private communication. National Vegetable Research Station, Wellesbourne, Warwickshire.

APPARENT SPECIFIC GRAVITY OR BULK DENSITY

This is a measure of the weight of a unit volume of the whole soil including the pore spaces. It can thus be used to compute the volume of the latter; its main function is in the calculation of available soil water on a volumetric basis for use in practical irrigation. Pebbles and stones present a difficulty in determining apparent specific gravity. Obviously they differ from the soil proper because they contain no available water. If they are to be excluded it is necessary to decide how small is a stone; in very stony soils it is usual to make allowances for stones above 2 mm diameter but this is a purely arbitrary dimension. The difficulty emphasises the artificial nature of the available water concept. If porous stones are present the volume of water they can contain is determined separately and added proportionately to the available water capacity of the profile.

THE INFLUENCE OF STRUCTURE ON AVAILABLE WATER CAPACITY

Soil structure is the name given to the more or less temporary aggregation of the ultimate soil particles into crumbs and blocks easily visible to the naked eye. Structure is influenced not only by size and shape of the basic particles defined by the term 'texture' but also by temporary additions such as the fibrous material of dead roots following the ploughing-in of a ley, and the addition of peat, green trash, farmyard manure and similar materials. Such materials increase the available water capacity by reason of their own porosity or sponginess, but they also affect available water capacity by binding together the mineral particles and thus influencing the pore-space of the soil.

These effects are temporary, disappearing as the added organic matter breaks down and changing as the growing season advances. In ephemeral horticultural crops, the soil consolidates as the crop grows, the apparent specific gravity changes, and the available water capacity is reduced. One of the functions of ploughing after such a crop is to restore the apparent specific gravity and hence available water capacity to its proper level (table 3.5 and table 9.2 page 120).

Table 3.5

Changes in bulk density and available water capacity of a sandy loam as the season advances

	With farmyard manure		Without farmyard manure	
	Bulk density	Available water capacity mm/0.3 m	Bulk density	Available water capacity mm/0.3 m
March	1.37	46	1.44	40
June	1.42	35	1.48	32
August	1.41	34	1.47	32
September	1.48	39	1.61	38
November	1.50	39	1.57	39

Data of Salter, P. J. (1967). Effect of farmyard manure on matric suction in sandy loam soil. *J. Soil Sci.* **18**, 2.

THE ENERGY CONCEPT OF SOIL WATER

The foregoing discussion may be summarised in terms of the energy associated with the soil water.

The potential energy of water in mass liquid form can be regarded as unity. The potential energy of the water in soil is less than this for six reasons. Firstly, adsorption of water onto the surfaces of the soil particles; secondly capillary attraction which results from the surface tension of the curved water films among the soil particles; thirdly electrical attraction of water molecules and ions at the charged surface of the clay particles in the soil. These three are difficult to measure separately, but their sum, the matric potential, is measured in the pressure membrane apparatus (see page 56) and in the osmometer. The terms 'matric potential', 'matric suction' and 'soil moisture tension' mean the same thing, though these terms are based on different concepts of the soil water. The fourth source of reduction is the osmotic potential which results from the presence of dissolved salts in the soil water. The total of matric potential and osmotic potential is measured in a thermocouple psychrometer (see page 57) and hence osmotic potential itself can be assessed by difference.

Next is hydrostatic potential which results from the weight of the column of water connecting the soil particles above the point of measurement. This is usually calculated theoretically from hydraulic principles. Finally there is a factor due to gravity which can be ignored when all the components are in the same gravitational field. All these forces contribute to reduction of the soil water potential relative to that of water in bulk; reduction of potential energy manifests itself in the soil water system as a suction which can be conveniently expressed in terms of negative pressure units, that is, negative bars, but conventionally the negative sign is usually omitted.

THE MEASUREMENT OF SOIL MOISTURE PARAMETERS

Soil water content

Samples are taken with a 25 mm (1 in) auger, usually at 100 mm (or 6 in) depth increments, and the appropriate borings from three or more holes are mixed to provide a representative sample weighing about 150 g. The sample is weighed, dried in a ventilated oven at 105°C for 4.5 h and re-weighed. It is then replaced in the oven for a further half hour and weighed again. If there has been no further weight change the moisture percentage of the original sample can be calculated. Water in soil is properly expressed on a volume basis and so the weight percentage is converted to volume percentage according to the apparent specific gravity of the soil as it is in the field.

Apparent specific gravity, or bulk density

A horizontal flat soil surface at the required depth is prepared by scraping, not by compression. A steel cylinder having a sharpened rim is carefully pressed vertically into the soil through a hole in a flat plate resting on the soil. The dry weight of the soil which exactly fills the cylinder, divided by the cylinder volume, gives the soil apparent specific gravity or bulk density. An alternative method is to excavate a hole in the flattened soil

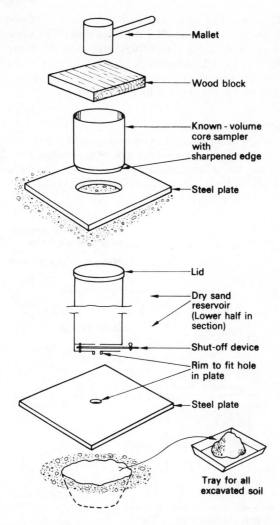

Figure 3.10 Apparatus for alternative methods of determining soil bulk density.

surface, carefully collecting every crumb of excavated soil for drying and weighing. The excavated hole is then exactly filled with dry sand from a sand reservoir fitted with a suitable shut-off device. The weight of sand filling the hole is determined by weighing the reservoir before and after use; the volume/weight ratio of the sand is known from calibration and hence the volume of the hole can be calculated (see figure 3.10).

Bulk density can be determined on clods of 50 − 200 ml volume, selected in the field and immediately coated with a waterproof film such as rubber latex, paraffin wax, or polyvinyl chloride. The volume of the coated clod can then be measured by the usual water displacement method after which it can be broken open and oven-dried for moisture determination. In the US Department of Agriculture a synthetic resin is used as the coating film; this material is permeable to water vapour but not to liquid water so that the clod can be dried intact.

Water infiltration rate

The rate at which water enters a soil may be judged roughly by noting the rate of drainage from a water-filled bottomless metal cylinder, about 0.25 m diameter, thrust into the undisturbed soil surface. Because water is moving laterally as well as downwards from the zone of wetted soil this method is of limited value.

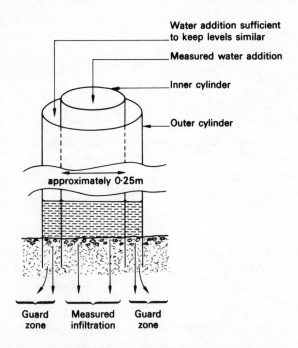

Figure 3.11   Method for measuring infiltration rate of water into soil.

A better method is to use two concentric cylinders, keeping the water at approximately the same level in each and measuring the input rate to the centre cylinder needed to keep its water level constant (figure 3.11). Infiltration rate is governed mainly by particle size (texture) of the soil; in a medium sand it may be about 600 mm per hour, in a medium loam about 40 and in a clay only about 20 mm per hour.

Hydraulic conductivity or permeability

Mass flow of water within the soil may be measured in the field by sinking a tube of about 30 mm bore to within about 100 mm of the bottom of a hole of slightly larger bore. The cavity below the tube is filled with coarse sand while the annular space between tube and bore is sealed with waterproof bentonite clay. The rate at which water pumped out of the tube is replaced from below represents the hydraulic conductivity of the soil horizon level with the bottom of the tube. This technique is especially useful for measuring the effects of pans and horizons of impeded drainage. Hydraulic conductivity can also be measured in the laboratory by arranging a simple apparatus to run deaerated water vertically through a

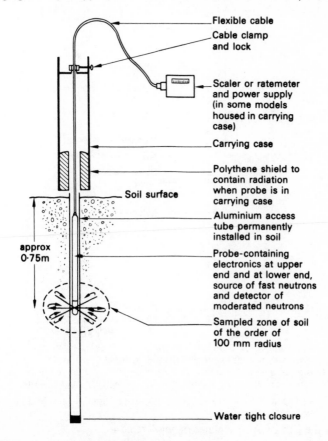

Figure 3.12 General arrangement of typical 'neutron probe'. The probe is lowered to the required depth within the access tube and the rate of return of moderated neutrons measured, or better, their number is summed over a precisely-measured period of about a minute.

saturated soil core preferably at constant head and measuring the equilibrium flow rate.

Soil permeability ranges from less than 50 mm per day in a clay up to 10 m per day in a coarse sand.

Soil water content *in situ*

In the neutron moderation method a source of fast neutrons, the neutron probe, is lowered into the soil down a permanently sited access tube which is usually about 50 mm bore (figure 3.12). Fast neutrons travel in straight lines but on contact with hydrogen nuclei they are slowed, or moderated, and then travel with random motion. A detector near the neutron source

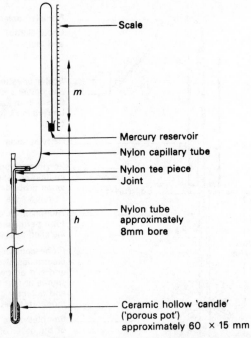

Scale

m

Mercury reservoir
Nylon capillary tube
Nylon tee piece
Joint

Nylon tube approximately 8mm bore

h

Ceramic hollow 'candle' ('porous pot') approximately 60 × 15 mm

Figure 3.13 General arrangement of Webster's (1966) tensiometer. The whole system is filled with airfree water by injecting it through the upper bung of the tee piece. Tension in mm water equals the height of mercury column (m) multiplied by 127, less difference in level (*h*), in mm of surface of mercury and porous pot.

Webster, R., (1966). The measurement of soil water tension in the field. *New Phyt.* **65**, 249–58.

senses the density of the cloud of moderated neutrons which is related to the concentration of hydrogen nuclei in the soil; the probe does not distinguish between hydrogen of the soil water and that, for instance, in organic matter and it is sensitive to differences in density of the soil. Hence it must be calibrated for different circumstances.

The neutron scattering method is regarded as the best technique for determining soil moisture status and it has the great advantage that successive measurements are made on the same soil without any disturbance. The method is especially suitable for following soil moisture changes in the profile with time; for this absolute calibration is not necessary (see figure 4.3, page 64).

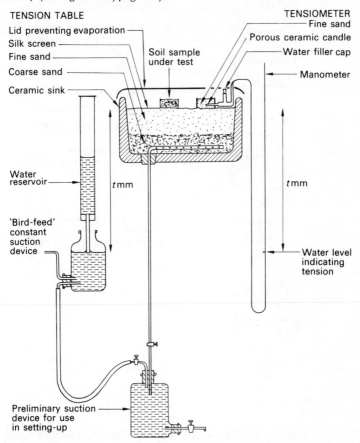

Figure 3.14 Sand tension table. To set up, the sink is filled with water and first coarse and then fine sand added so that they settle under water; air is removed by manipulating the stopcocks. The 'bird-feed' constant suction device (left) is lowered to produce the required tension which is checked at the sand surface by the horizontal tensiometer (right). The soil samples in bottomless metal cylinders are placed on the sand surface to come to moisture equilibrium and then their moisture content is determined gravimetrically.

Wilkinson, B. (1972). Private communication. M.A.F.F. Agricultural Development and Advisory Service, Shardlow Hall, Derby.

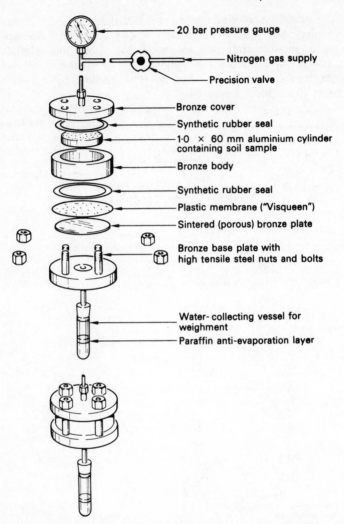

Figure 3.15 Exploded view (above) of typical individual-sample pressure membrane apparatus. Chambers capable of holding several samples are also available.
   The assembled apparatus is shown below.

Soil moisture characteristic release curve

A soil sample, preferably undisturbed (see page 60), is completely wetted by keeping it in a saturated atmosphere or by placing it on a tension table (figure 3.14). By altering the level of the suction control the tension table itself can be used to obtain points on the release curve up to 0.1 bar (10 kN m^{-2}). For higher suctions pressure membrane apparatus is needed (figure 3.15). The sample is placed on a cellulose membrane in a suitable vessel and a pressure of nitrogen gas is applied to the surface; water is forced out of the sample until its matric potential equals the gas pressure. Equilibrium is judged to have been achieved when there is no further change in weight of the water-collecting vessel. The moisture content of the sample may then be determined gravimetrically to give one point on the required curve. If an individual pressure vessel is used for each sample, the pressure can be raised successively between equilibrations to give a series of points without removing the sample and a single moisture determination can be made at the end; the intermediate moisture contents can be computed from this by adding the weight of water collected at each pressure increment.

Other methods for measuring soil moisture based on radioactive techniques use gamma and beta radiation.

Electrical resistance or capacitance methods depend on changes in electrical properties of porous material embedded in the soil, resulting from changes in moisture content. The resistance method is affected by the presence of electrolytes (fertilisers) in the soil water, and is more suited to sensing the location of an advancing wetted front than to absolute measurements of soil moisture.

In the thermal method a known quantity of heat is fed into the soil from a buried electrical heater; the rate of dissipation of heat after the source is switched off is measured using thermocouples or thermistors and this can then be related to soil water content.

Soil moisture tension (matric potential)

The tensiometer is a water-filled porous pot embedded in the soil. Water moves in or out of the pot until pressure equilibrium with the soil water potential is achieved. The resulting suction inside the pot is measured mechanically using a suction gauge, hydrostatically using a mercury or water manometer, or electrically using a strain gauge or a pressure sensor; a typical design is shown in figure 3.13. Several different forms of tensiometer have been marketed for use in commercial horticulture.

Soil pF curve

A soil sample at the required moisture content is allowed to come into vapour equilibrium with the air in a small container at constant temperature. The vapour pressure of the enclosed air and hence the total water potential including the osmotic pressure of the sample is then measured. A very small thermocouple inside the chamber is cooled by passing a small current through it; the cooling causes a drop of water to condense upon the thermocouple (the Peltier effect). When the current is switched off the water begins to evaporate, cooling the thermocouple in relation to the heat sink formed by the thick wires leading to it; this causes a very small current to flow which is proportional to the cooling and hence to the vapour pressure of the air and the total water potential of the sample.

There are many variants of this delicate apparatus, usually known as the thermocouple psychrometer, which can be used for measuring the water potential of any suitable sample, including plant material.

Field capacity

Gravimetric determination of soil moisture content (see page 50) is made on samples taken when the soil appears, from observation, to be at field capacity. The best results are obtained when the soil has come naturally to field capacity, for example early spring in the UK. At other seasons a timber frame about one metre square and 0.1 metre deep is placed on the soil and filled with water which is allowed to percolate into the soil. A waterproof cover prevents evaporation and after 48 h or longer, when drainage is considered to have reverted to the slow rate, soil samples are taken for gravimetric determination of their moisture content.

Field capacity may also be measured in the laboratory. Samples are brought to moisture equilibrium at 0.1 bar ($10 \, kN \, m^{-2}$) on the tension table, or sand table (figure 3.14) or at 0.33 bar ($33 \, kN \, m^{-2}$) using pressure membrane apparatus (figure 3.15) whichever is regarded as equivalent to field capacity for the particular soil. The equilibrium moisture content is then determined gravimetrically.

Resin-coated clods (see page 51) can be brought to field capacity by cutting a window in the resin coating through which the clod can be brought into contact with the wet sand of a tension table and moisture-equilibrated at 0.1 bar; after equilibration the window can be painted over with more resin and the moisture content of the clod determined gravimetrically.

Permanent wilting point

A suitable plant, usually sunflower, is grown in a soil sample of about 200 ml contained in a watertight tin. When the roots are judged to have filled completely the whole sample the soil surface is sealed with a watertight cap or with wax, and no further water is applied. The plant is examined daily, and when its first pair of true leaves is seen to have wilted, the culture is placed in a saturated atmosphere (a belljar containing a pan of water). If the leaves do *not* regain turgidity the soil is assumed to be at permanent wilting point and its moisture content is determined gravimetrically (figure 3.16).

To determine wilting point in the laboratory a soil sample is brought to moisture equilibrium at 15 bar ($1.5 \, MN \, m^{-2}$) in the pressure membrane apparatus (figure 3.15) and its moisture content determined gravimetrically.

Figure 3.16 Sunflower method for determining permanent wilting point. Left, intact plant ready for test; others, with cotyledons and apices removed and soil covered with impermeable foil. When they had wilted the plants were placed in a saturated atmosphere. The soil of the right-hand culture is at permanent wilting point; that of the centre culture is not.

Available water capacity

In the literature this will usually be found expressed on a volume basis in units of millimetres of water per 100 millimetres depth of soil, or inches of water per foot depth.

$$AWC = \frac{(FC - PWP) \times ASG \times depth}{100}$$

where

AWC	=	available water capacity
FC	=	field capacity
PWP	=	permanent wilting point
ASG	=	apparent specific gravity (bulk density)

However, it is more useful to express available water capacity as a dimensionless ratio. Thus AWC of 1/12 or 0.83 can readily be converted into whatever units are convenient for the particular need, and becomes 1 in. per 12 in. soil depth, 10 mm per 120 mm or 0.8 in. per 10 in., 8 mm per 0.1 m.

A rapid method for rough assessment of available water capacity in the field is described on page 46).

Soil samples

Soil augers of 20 − 50 mm diameter, similar to those used by carpenters, are convenient for extracting samples of soil from depths down to 0.75 m. The broken-up samples are suitable for measurement of moisture content and for chemical analysis. However, many workers have shown that results for field capacity, permanent wilting point and hence available water capacity, matric potential by the pressure membrane method and pF by the psychrometer method are all more consistent and closer to expected values if they are made on undisturbed samples (monolith cores) instead of on loose soil. So-called undisturbed samples are obtained by carefully forcing into a surface prepared in the field soil a suitably sized hollow cylinder and then excavating this without disturbing the soil inside, and leaving undisturbed soil protruding from each end. The surplus is then pared away in the laboratory prior to placing the sample in the appropriate apparatus, with its structure unchanged from the field condition.

For examination of unbroken cores, and for extraction of root samples, a Veihmeyer tube may be used. This has a circular cutting edge whose inside diameter is one or two mm less than the bore of the tube on which it is mounted. Thus the cylinder of soil which it cuts on being forced vertically into the field soil passes up into the sampling tube without being compressed.

SUMMARY OF CHAPTER 3

The potential associated with soil water is termed soil moisture tension, and may be expressed as millimetres of water or mercury suction, that is, the suction exerted at the top of an unsupported column of water or mercury of the specified height. The tensiometer measures matric potential in these terms. Measurement of total potential requires rather sophisticated apparatus but as under normal conditions osmotic potential is negligible, matric potential measured with tensiometers or pressure membrane equipment can be equated with total potential. The potential energy of the soil water is zero at saturation, 0.1 − 0.33 bars at field capacity and 15 bars at permanent wilting point.

The pF curve expresses total potential; the characteristic, or soil moisture release characteristic curve, expresses matric potential.

Chapter 3 gives a gross simplification of a complex subject, beset by an involved and not always consistent terminology derived from different scientific disciplines, and the student of fundamental soil physics is referred to the extensive specialist literature.

CHAPTER 4

MOVEMENT OF WATER IN SOIL

Water may enter the rhizosphere† from above as natural or artificial precipitation, or as surface flow; water may enter the rhizosphere from below or from the sides by capillarity or movement along a gradient of potential, or by mass flow along a hydrostatic potential.

Entry from above is governed by the infiltration rate or percolation rate of the particular soil. This differs for different soil textures and may be altered by changes in soil structure, which can be brought about by suitable horticultural management. If water arrives on the soil surface at a rate exceeding the maximum infiltration rate, this results in runoff, damage to the soil structure, reduction in infiltration rate and consequent further increase in rate of runoff. Should the precipitation be in the form of large drops with high kinetic energy this too can damage soil structure and reduce infiltration rate. An extreme example is afforded by the state of the soil surface under the canopy of low-growing shrubs, subjected to repeated battering by heavy dripping from the foliage; such a soil has a hard almost impervious cement-like cap unless appropriate horticultural remedial measures such as admixture of peat have been taken.

The horticultural significance of runoff, resulting from excess of water arrival over infiltration rate is that water which might otherwise have entered the rhizosphere to be used by roots or to drain through into storage layers of the soil, is entirely lost from the plant—soil system. Only in the case of furrow irrigation is surface flow beneficial; here, if the flow of water into the furrow is less than the infiltration rate all the water will penetrate the furrow bottom and none will reach the far end.

EROSION

Damage to the soil structure caused by the impact of large drops consists first of slaking, or breakdown of the soil crumbs into an amorphous slurry; this pastelike material eventually covers the soil surface. It is resistant to the passage of water through it. On sloping land the slurry is pulled by gravity over the surface in the initial phase of erosion. As more water falls, the moving slurry is diluted and its speed of movement increased so that runnels begin to be eroded into the soil beneath. This phenomenon has special significance in spray irrigation where the drop size must be kept small enough to avoid damage to the soil structure and the application rate must be less than the soil infiltration rate. Different soils can accept different drop sizes and different application rates.

† Strictly the rhizosphere is the zone of soil immediately surrounding and under the influence of an individual root; here the term is used as a convenient way of referring to the zone of soil influenced by the whole root system.

CAPPING

After cessation of excessive precipitation the film of slurry left on the soil surface constitutes a cap. If this cap remains wet, or can be kept wet by very light irrigation with fine drops, it does not interfere unduly with emergence of seedlings, but it can interfere with entry of both air and water into the soil, and hence with establishment and growth (figure 4.1). Should the cap become dry, small seedlings are unable to penetrate it although air and water can readily enter the soil through discrete cracks which result from shrinkage on drying (figure 4.2).

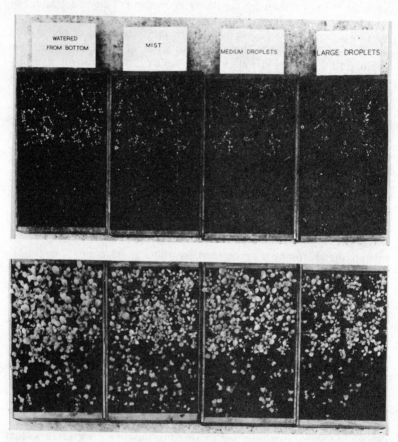

Figure 4.1   Seedboxes sown with identical numbers of lettuce seeds (upper parts of boxes) and of cabbage (lower parts), and then watered as indicated.
Top row — after one week the soil surface has dried; notice the different degrees of damage to the soil structure and the effect of this on emergence.
Bottom row — the same boxes after two weeks showing differences in growth of the seedlings.

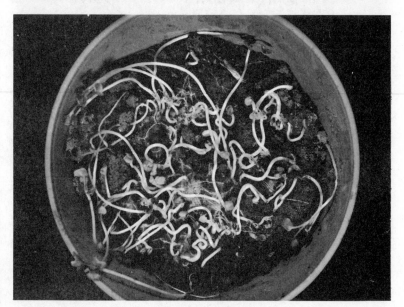

Figure 4.2 Pots of sandy loam soil on which a cap was produced by heavily watering with large drops until slaking had occurred. Above, previously-sown radish seedlings emerging through a crack in the dried cap; below, the cap removed to show seedlings which have been unable to penetrate the hard cap.

WATER MOVEMENT IN SATURATED SOIL

Once in the soil water moves at a rate governed by the hydraulic conductivity of the soil, and in response to gradients in water hydraulic potential. Water movement in soil is referred to as redistribution.

In a saturated soil hydraulic conductivity is maximal and hence the rate of infiltration and downward movement equals the rate at which water is falling on the surface, up to the maximum set by the conductivity of the particular soil. The same applies to the sideways movement of water during furrow irrigation. Water moves in mass flow amongst the soil particles in response to gradients in hydrostatic pressure at the soil surface or in the irrigation furrow, or by the upsurgence of a rising water table. Water moving in laterally from the side of a furrow irrigated bed is deflected by gravity so that the resultant flow is at an angle to the horizontal, governed by the hydraulic conductivity of the soil — the more porous or sandy the soil, the more will water tend to flow downwards rather than sideways. This sets a limit to the width of beds to be watered from furrows alongside them; beds in sandy soil must be narrower than beds in heavier soils.

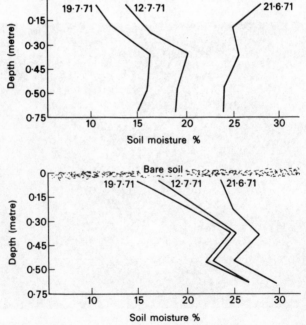

Figure 4.3   Changes in soil moisture content during 28 days, measured by the neutron scattering method ('neutron probe'). The grass roots have denuded the whole profile whereas from bare soil most of the evaporative loss has been from the surface layer.

One method of circumventing damage to soil structure caused by impact or flow is to apply the water slowly at discrete points so that only the soil immediately below the point of application becomes wetted. Downward saturated flow takes place together with a sideways component whose magnitude again depends upon the hydraulic conductivity of the particular soil. In a sandy soil the resultant wetted cone is deep and narrow; in a heavier soil it is wider and shallower. This principle is exploited in trickle irrigation systems for use in glasshouses and for watering individual trees in the open (figure 9.5).

THE WETTED FRONT

Water arriving on the soil surface brings each successive layer to saturation before appreciable further downward movement takes place. Thus in an unsaturated soil, if there is sufficient precipitation to saturate, for example, only the top 100 mm, then virtually no water at all penetrates beyond about 150 mm; the 50 mm extra penetration represents, in the soil under consideration, the extra depth of soil which will be brought to field capacity when drainage from the saturated top 100 mm brings that soil to field capacity. In irrigation practice this means that it is not possible to raise the water content of a soil to any value except saturation and subsequent field capacity. Any attempt to wet a soil only partially, by reducing the quantity of water applied, merely reduces the *depth* of soil which is brought to field capacity.

THE WATER TABLE

A water table is a zone of saturated soil or rock in which the water potential is maximal; it is usually caused by the presence of an impermeable stratum which may be continuous over a large area, or it may result from the presence of a concave basin of impermeable material with permeable material above and below, when it is known as a perched water table. A water table at ten metres or more is beyond the reach of the roots of normal plants, but the closer it is to the surface the more influence a water table has on the water supply to root systems.

The nearer a water table is to the surface, the greater is the risk of its being harmful instead of beneficial. For example, in areas of high evaporation rate, water moving upwards from the water table evaporates from the soil surface, leaving behind its salt burden to accumulate perhaps in disastrous concentration; conditions can be improved only by draining to lower the water table, followed by copious flooding to bring about leaching of the harmful salts. Furthermore, the nearer the water table is to the surface, the smaller is the volume of soil available for exploitation by the root system and hence the greater is the risk of drought should the water table fall temporarily.

These harmful influences can be corrected by judicious drainage, but in peat soils where high water tables are common, drainage must be done with caution for fear of causing the whole peat mass to shrink and sink and become prone to uncontrollable seasonal flooding. Yet another risk attendant upon drainage of peat land is that the surface peat may dry out completely; peat is difficult to re-wet once it has become air dry.

IMPEDED DRAINAGE

Zones of excessively high water potential may also occur in soils where there is no coherent layer sufficiently impermeable to create a water table. They can result, for example, from slaking and downward migration of clay particles to accumulate in pockets; these are easily recognised by a blue-grey discolouration in the profile, and sometimes a distinctive odour. The macrostructure of heavy soils can be damaged by repeatedly ploughing at the same depth, when polishing of the furrow bottom reduces its permeability to water and its penetrability by roots.

Such zones of impeded drainage, sometimes called pans, can cause local waterlogging and can lengthen the time of persistence of saturation of the surface soil after heavy precipitation. The harmful effect of such waterlogging lies in reduction of soil aeration and hence interference with root respiration; damage to subsequent crop growth has been detected following waterlogging for only a few hours. Thus the usual recommendation always to fill to the brim when watering potted plants is safe only when the growing medium is freely draining.

On the other hand excessive drainage through a field soil can have its own harmful effect; nutrients in the soil can be dissolved in the drainage water and leached or transported out of reach of the roots. This is one reason for applying frequent small dressings of fertiliser in preference to a single large application.

WATER MOVEMENT IN UNSATURATED SOIL

In unsaturated soil, conductivity is governed by the soil moisture status (see page 38) and the computation of flow rate is complex. Theoretically, as described in chapter 3, some downward movement of water continues at a very slow rate virtually indefinitely but major movements in unsaturated soil occur mainly in response to moisture potential gradients; water moves from wet zones to drier ones. Entry of water into a root or evaporation from the soil surface sets up a gradient which causes water to move from soil particle to particle towards the denuded zone.

By the same token, upward movement from a water table can be appreciable, though slow compared with mass flow rates. In a sandy loam about 10 mm per day has been found to move upwards from a water table at 1 m depth; when the water table was lowered to 3 m the rate of upward unsaturated movement fell to only 1 mm per day. These are maximum rates dependent on water being removed from the upper end of the potential gradient by evaporation or uptake into roots.

This phenomenon has been exploited in the capillary sand bench for the automatic watering of pot plants (see page 126) where a water table is maintained 25–50 mm below the roots in the pots. Here the maximum possible rate of capillary movement exceeds the evaporation and transpiration rate and the soil remains permanently at field capacity, water being replaced as fast as it is removed from the growing medium.

EVAPORATION FROM SOIL

Water evaporates from a wet surface using energy derived directly from the sun's radiation, or advective energy brought in by air moving over the wet surface (see chapter 8). The rate of evaporation from wet soil is substantially the same as that from an open water surface and this rate of evaporation continues as long as supplies are maintained at the foot of the potential gradient thus set up. The hydraulic conductivity falls rapidly as the soil moisture content falls (as the fourth power of the moisture content) so that quite suddenly a dry layer forms on the soil surface. Evaporation then virtually ceases. In a sandy soil this happens when about 12 mm of water have been lost from the top 200 mm of soil, in a heavier soil when about 20 mm have been lost from the top 300 mm.

In early summer, when the bare soil surface appears bone dry, moist soil will be found a few centimetres down and if the soil is undisturbed and there are no plants growing in it, this state will continue almost indefinitely. If the land is heavily cultivated, wet soil brought to the surface will dry in its turn and the net result will be loss of valuable stored water from the profile. Water will also be lost from the profile if weeds are allowed to become established (figure 4.3). Cultivation should be avoided until absolutely necessary, weeds being killed chemically, and should then be kept to the minimum needed to prepare the required seedbed or planting bed.

MEASUREMENT OF SOIL WATER MOVEMENT

Runoff

A trough, such as a length of rainwater guttering, is positioned along the lower edge of the soil slope to be investigated. A strip of polyethylene sheet is placed with one edge in the gutter and the other buried in the soil on its upslope side; this traps the runoff by leading it over the lip of the gutter and preventing it eroding a way beneath. The trough is covered with a strip of some rigid material to prevent rain falling directly into it. The volume of water collected in a raingauge on the plot is then compared with the volume of water collected in the trough (a ditch or other barrier at the top of the soil slope ensures that the trough collects only runoff from the plot itself).

Erosion

The outfall from a trough similar to that described above is led through a series of settling tanks where different particle size fractions of eroded material separate out and can be collected for weighing (figure 4.4).

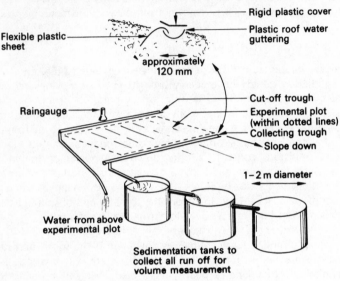

Figure 4.4   Equipment for measuring runoff and erosion.

Water movement within soil

The progress of a wetting front can be followed by observing sudden changes in the readings of an array of tensiometers, electrical resistance blocks or other sensors as the water reaches them. The neutron probe is especially suitable for studies of this kind and enables a detailed picture of changes in water status throughout the profile to be built up over long periods (see figure 4.3, page 64).

Drainage

Observation of field drain outfalls enables records to be made of the date when they begin to discharge ('run') and of the volume of water discharged per unit time. This can be related to the area of land served by the drainage system and to its state of saturation, or field capacity. Instruments are available for making such records automatically. Because of soil heterogeneity and variation in depth and condition of the drains it is essential to average the results obtained from many outfalls from the drains under a given area.

Hydraulic conductivity or permeability

Mass flow of water within the soil may be measured in the field by sinking a tube about 30 mm bore to within about 100 mm of the bottom of a hole of slightly larger bore. The cavity below the tube is filled with coarse sand while the annular space between tube and bore is sealed with waterproof bentonite clay. The rate at which water pumped out of the tube is replaced from below represents the hydraulic conductivity of the soil horizon level with the bottom of the tube. This technique is especially useful for measuring the effects of pans and horizons of impeded drainage.

Hydraulic conductivity can also be measured in the laboratory by arranging simple apparatus to run de-aerated water vertically through a saturated soil core preferably at constant head, and measuring the equilibrium flow rate. Soil permeability ranges from less than 50 mm per day in a clay up to 10 m per day in a coarse sand.

SUMMARY OF CHAPTER 4

Entry of water into a soil is governed by the infiltration rate and the state of the soil surface; both of these can be harmed by bad soil management.

If precipitation rate exceeds infiltration rate the resultant runoff not only wastes water but also can cause irreparable damage by erosion.

Water movement in saturated soil is governed by hydraulic conductivity and the water moves along gradients of hydrostatic pressure.

Penetration of soil by water proceeds only as each successive layer is saturated. It is not possible by adding water at the surface to raise the moisture content of soil to any level other than saturation. Altering the quantity of water added merely alters the depth of soil brought to the state of saturation.

Water tables may be beneficial or harmful; drainage of peatland must be cautiously planned for fear of causing the whole area to sink.

Water movement in unsaturated soil is governed by the soil moisture status; upward movement by capillarity is appreciable but slow.

Evaporation takes place from bare wet soil at about the same rate as from an open water surface; evaporation from dry bare soil is negligible.

CHAPTER 5

THE HYDROLOGICAL STRUCTURE
OF VASCULAR PLANTS

For details of the anatomy and histology of vascular plants the reader is referred to the many specialist textbooks; in this book the plant is considered as a system of plumbing, the efficient operation of which depends upon different components whose functions may not be immediately apparent from their structure.

The plant contains two almost independent transport systems; the phloem which is living carries metabolites mainly downwards from the foliage, and to and from storage organs, while the xylem consisting mainly of dead tissue, brings water and nutrients up from the roots. The two systems merge in young tissues and there are cross connections, the medullary rays, in most parts of the stems. Here we are concerned with the water-transporting system only, the xylem and its ancillary organs and tissues disposed throughout the roots, stems and leaves.

THE WATER-CONDUCTING VESSELS

These are built up from rows of large elongated dead cells whose side walls have become thickened and waterproofed in different ways and with distinctive patterns of pores left in them; the transverse cell walls have disintegrated so that the net result is a series of tubes communicating directly between the source of water in the root and its ultimate destination, the atmosphere surrounding the foliage. The vessels end blindly at their lower extremities among the absorbing cells of the roots, and at their upper ends among the photosynthetic cells of the leaves. A few end immediately beneath hydathodes and lenticels. In perennial plants the vessels of only the outermost layer of wood communicate with the current season's leaves; the inner wood is no longer concerned with water conduction.

Among the vessels in the xylem are shorter almost solid fibres which apparently have a purely mechanical function, and living parenchymatous cells comprising the medullary rays. The latter communicate between the vessels and tissues in the outer parts of the stem including the phloem whence they extract materials for temporary storage.

ROOTS

The ultimate organs of the roots connecting with the soil are the root hairs; each is a protuberance from a single cell of the epidermis. The root hairs are in intimate contact with the soil particles and penetrate crevices within them; they are shortlived and disappear after a few days to be replaced by new ones formed immediately behind the advancing root tip. Root hairs are not essential to the plant for they are often absent when a plant is grown under abnormal conditions, as for example in water culture. Root hairs are produced in profusion in a moist aerobic atmosphere such as immediately above the surface in a water culture.

Each root terminates in a growing point surmounted by a more or less distinct root cap which is a covering of mucilaginous cells said to aid progress of the growing root by lubricating the soil crumbs. The terminal part of the root is usually white or transparent; further back the surface of the root becomes suberised and darker in colour. It was formerly supposed that roots did not absorb water from the soil in this older region but there is now evidence that absorption can and does take place almost anywhere within the rhizosphere and for that matter in the foliage also. About 70 per cent of the total water absorption by the root system of a herbaceous plant takes place through the brown more or less suberised regions.

THE ROOT SYSTEM

The appearance and conformation of the root system depends much on external conditions; the absence of root hairs in water culture has already been mentioned. Bean plants grown in water culture have white fleshy roots, whereas in the field they have thin brown, branched fibrous roots. It has been suggested that crops grown with plentiful water supplies tend to produce root systems confined to the surface soil whereas crops with indifferent water supplies are deeper rooting. Some evidence of this has been produced (figure 6.1) but there is often more variation among root systems *within* a given watering treatment than between average rooting depths of groups of plants given contrasting watering treatments. On the other hand tea plants grown in deep well-drained soil produce deep root systems but when grown in peat bogs the roots are confined to the surface.

The total length and rate of growth of roots furnish convenient parameters for comparing the performance of plants under different treatments. Root systems are difficult to extract completely from soil and their extraordinary complexity may be judged from reliable results in which the total lengths of the root systems of single lettuce plants were estimated to be of the order of 300 m.

Adventitious roots may arise almost anywhere on the plant and do not differ in structure or function from the primary roots which arose from the seedling radicle. In some plants, such as cereals, adventitious roots largely supplant the tap root system as the plant matures, whereas in vegetatively propagated plants such as sugar cane, pelargonium, potatoes and tea, the whole root system is of course adventitious.

The rhizosphere is mainly confined to a volume of moist soil sufficient to meet the transpiration demand of the current foliage; as the soil is denuded of water, roots tend to grow outwards along gradients of moisture availability but the facility still remains to take in water from anywhere within the previously exploited zone should this become rewetted.

Many plants produce a few abnormally large fleshy roots ranging far beyond their main dense root systems, often to remarkable depths in the subsoil. In cauliflower and turnip such roots have been found more than three metres deep. The function of these deep ranging roots is not known, and the plants will grow properly in pots without them. The critical and difficult experiment of finding them in open soil and cutting them without damaging the rest of the root system has yet to be performed. To suggest that they are an insurance against drought is to impute purpose to the plant; the fact remains that they grow far beyond the immediate effects of the water and nutrient gradients which influence the growth of the rest of the root system.

The vascular bundles in young root systems are arranged radially with the phloem and xylem alongside one another, whereas in the stem the phloem is disposed outside the xylem; the changeover takes place in the hypocotyl region.

In the upper parts of older roots and the lower parts of stems are found lenticels, pores fixed in size and shape and usually loosely filled with dead cellular material. Their function is said to be respiratory and certainly they become enlarged and swollen in waterlogged soil, of which this phenomenon is diagnostic.

STEMS AND FOLIAGE

Stems support the photosynthetic and reproductive organs in the environment' appropriate to their different functions, and house the transport systems communicating between them and the roots.

Foliage consists of usually green stems and leaves. The structure of the leaf reflects its all-important function of photosynthesis. On the upper surface immediately beneath the epidermis is the palisade parenchyma consisting of closely packed cells furnished with chloroplasts. Between these and the lower epidermis is a zone of loosely packed cells having air spaces between them, the spongy parenchyma, also photosynthetic. Leading from the spaces in the spongy parenchyma to the atmosphere outside the leaf are the stomatal pores. Some species, such as *Nasturtium*, have multicellular pores, fixed in size and located usually at the tips of leaves near to the terminations of main vascular bundles (veins). Their function is not understood; when the plant is fully turgid and the atmospheric vapour pressure high, liquid water drops can be seen exuding from these hydathodes by a process called guttation.

STOMATA

Each stoma consists of a pair of elongated guard cells, occasionally supplemented as in grasses, with extra subsidiary cells. Unlike the rest of the epidermal cells the stomatal guard cells contain chloroplasts. The shape of the guard cells is such that when they are turgid their adjacent walls separate to form a pore. The shape and width of the pore determines its performance in permitting the passage of vapour and gases. The relationship between stomatal aperture and transpiration is discussed on page 94. The pore aperture diminishes proportionally with reduction in turgor pressure in the guard cells; when they are flaccid the stoma is fully closed. Stomata, several thousand per square centimetre, are usually confined to the undersides of leaves but in some species they may be present also on the upper surfaces, but in smaller numbers. In the floating leaves of water plants all the stomata are on the upper side. Stomata may be found on some stems but never on roots.

THE 'PLUMBING' SYSTEM

The water conducting system of a vascular plant thus consists of upper and lower groups of thin-walled living cells in intimate contact with the ends of thick-walled dead tubes which have pores communicating laterally with one another and with other tissues in the stems. At the lower end of the system the outermost thin-walled cells are touching the water films around the soil particles, while at the upper end the thin-walled cells form the boundaries of air cavities within the leaf; these cavities communicate with the outside atmosphere through pores which can close on receipt of appropriate stimuli. Thus in effect there is a continuous column of water connecting the soil water with the atmosphere, and having regulating mechanisms at each end (living cells, the passage of water through which depends on the osmotic potential of their contents and the water potential of the atmosphere or soil outside), and a secondary regulating mechanism (the stomata) interposed between the enclosed air and the outside atmosphere. Figure 5.1 shows a diagrammatic representation of this 'plumbing' system.

GENERAL CONFORMATION

The essential metabolism of the plant depends upon the leaves being held in such a posture that they will intercept the required amount of radiation (this is not always at right angles to the direction of the sunlight). Reproduction and seed dispersal likewise depend upon the appropriate organs being held in suitable postures for all the complicated processes of pollination, fruit ripening, dispersal and the like to take place. Usually these postures involve spreading the organs in the aerial environment on a system of branches originating on a major supporting structure, the

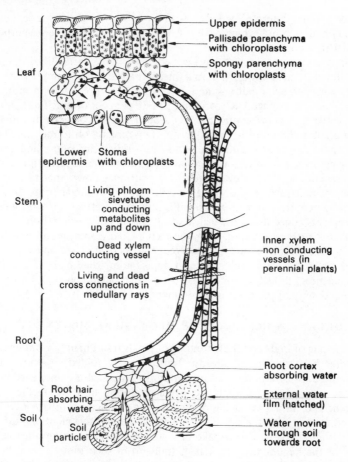

Figure 5.1 Diagrammatic representation of the 'plumbing' system of a vascular plant. For precise details of the structures named the reader should consult a textbook of histology.

mechanical strain on which may be considerable. The head of a 7 m high coconut palm is subjected to a lateral pressure of about 10 kg in a light 15 km/h breeze. At soil level the turning moment on the stem is of the order of 70 Nom; the turning moment at the crankshaft of a 3 litre sports car is about 20 Nom.

The stem is anchored in the soil either by means of a deep and rigid tap root, or more often by a copiously branched system of small roots.

In the young plant and the herbaceous adult plant the supporting system consists mainly of thin-walled turgid cells, quite distinct from the water conducting vessels and sometimes aided by fibres acting as internal guyropes. In the woody plant the required mechanical strength is derived mainly from internal woody vessels which were at one time water-conducting but which have lost that function and serve no purpose other than support.

In previous chapters we have considered entry of water into the soil with the tacit assumption that this meant bare soil, but the presence of plants considerably modifies the mode of entry of precipitation into the rhizosphere. In average UK woodland 25—30 per cent of precipitation has been shown to be intercepted by the canopy† and it is obvious that in any dense plant community little of the rain falls directly on to the soil. Once intercepted the water either falls to the ground in larger and more damaging drips from the foliage, or it passes down the surfaces of petioles and branches as 'stem-flow'. Such flow continues down the main stem below the soil surface and along the outsides of the larger roots. In arid locations stem-flow contributes significantly to the efficiency with which desert plants concentrate and utilise small amounts of precipitation.

Plants such as rhubarb, aloe, most cultivated graminae and brassicae have foliage structures such as enlarged stipules or grooved and flattened petioles which envelop the stem and appear to provide collecting points for stem flow, though whether this makes a significant contribution to the water economy of the plant is as yet unknown.

ORGANS WHICH PRODUCE MECHANICAL MOVEMENT

The opening of buds and the unfolding of petals result mainly from uptake of water by the cells of already formed closely folded structures; the fullsized petals of a poppy can readily be teased out of the unopened bud. On the other hand diurnal opening and closing of flowers, the slow scanning and the rapid coiling of tendrils, the closing of trifoliate leaves in rain or darkness and the rapid movements of the sensitive plant *Mimosa* all result from the reversible uptake of water by blocks of thin-walled cells. Many of the Leguminosae have pads (pulvini) of such thin-walled cells at their leaf bases which can cause spectacular movements of the whole leaf.

The mechanism of conduction of the stimulus which in *Mimosa pudica* travels at about 30 mm per second is unknown but it is tempting to suppose that it may be mere conduction of water within the vessels or from cell to cell in a pulvinus.

MEASUREMENT OF STOMATAL APERTURE

Replica or fascimile method

A thin film of quicksetting material such as nail varnish or rubber solution is painted on to the leaf surface; after setting, the replica bearing the impressions of the stomata is stripped off and examined under a microscope. Results should be interpreted with caution because the method assumes that the paint penetrates deep into the stomatal pits, and that setting takes place before the guard cells have had time to react.

† data of Leyton, L. (1972). Private communication. Department of Forestry, University of Oxford.

Cuticle strip method

A strip of cuticle, complete with stomata is peeled off the leaf and immediately fixed in alcohol prior to microscopic examination; this method also assumes that fixation takes place before the stomatal apertures change appreciably.

Infiltration method

A series of mixtures of liquids is prepared such that they present a regular gradation in mobility and hence will penetrate pores of certain sizes. Suitable pairs of liquids include kerosene and paraffin oil, isobutanol and ethylene glycol, and medicinal paraffin mixed with xylol, *n*-dodecane or *n*-tetradecane. Drops of each mixture in turn are placed upon the stomatal surface of the leaf to be investigated. When the stomata are wide open all the mixtures will penetrate the leaf surface into the intercellular spaces and the leaf will present a water-soaked appearance to the naked eye, around the point of application. When the stomata are closed none of the mixtures will enter. The mixture which just fails to enter indicates the degree of stomatal opening. The series of mixtures may be calibrated using a porometer.

Porometers

The porosity of the leaf surface may be measured by forcing air through a

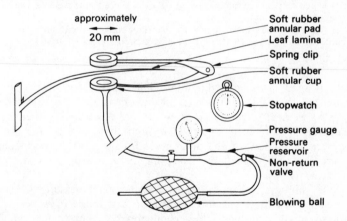

Figure 5.2 Principle of Alvim's (1965) pressure drop porometer. The soft annular pads are clipped on to a veinless part of the leaf. The purpose of the upper (open) pad is merely to hold the lower (closed) pad or cup in airtight contact with the stomata-bearing lower surface. A suitable pressure is raised in the air reservoir; the tap is then opened. The time for the pressure to fall to a given value is related to stomatal aperture.

Alvim, P. de T. (1965). A new type of porometer for measuring stomatal opening and its use in irrigation studies. In *Methodology of Eco-physiology* (Ed. F. E. Eckhardt), *Proc. Montpellier Symp. Arid Zone Res.* **25**, 325—9, Paris.

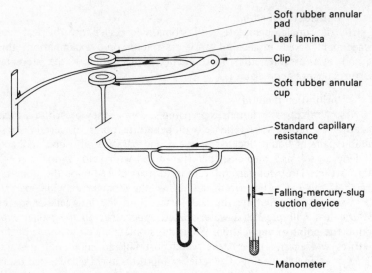

Soft rubber annular pad

Leaf lamina

Clip

Soft rubber annular cup

Standard capillary resistance

Falling-mercury-slug suction device

Manometer

Figure 5.3 Principle of Weatherley's (1966) suction porometer. Soft annular pads are clipped to a veinless part of the leaf. The lower closed pad forms a cup into which air is sucked through the stomata by the falling-mercury-slug suction device. The air passes through a standard capillary resistance, the pressure differential between the ends of which is related to the speed of airflow and hence to the stomatal aperture or leaf conductance.

The figure is diagrammatic; in practice the whole apparatus with the required taps is mounted in a single portable case. Details are given in the paper cited.

Weatherley, P. E. (1966). A porometer for use in the field *New Phyt.*, **62**, 376—87.

small enclosed zone into the intercellular spaces and thence to the atmosphere through the stomata in the unenclosed part of the leaf (Alvim's porometer, figure 5.2), or by sucking air in the reverse direction (Weatherley's porometer, figure 5.3). Both these instruments measure viscous or mass flow of the air. They must be calibrated for stomatal aperture by other methods and are best suited to comparative measurements.

Stiles' porometer (figure 5.4) on the other hand measures diffusive as opposed to mass flow and in one form at least its performance can be predicted mathematically, thus eliminating the need for empirical calibration. Its design and construction is more complex than that of the mass flow porometers but it measures diffusivity, the property of the leaf cuticle which directly influences vapour transfer (see page 95).

MEASUREMENT OF STEM FLOW

A sloping trough of modelling clay or similar waterproof plastic material is formed on the stem while it is dry. A small spout leads the collected stem

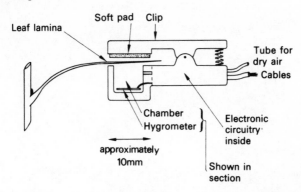

Figure 5.4 Stiles' (1970) diffusive resistance porometer. Within a small cup designed to be applied to the stomatal surface is an electrical resistance hygrometer and the thermistor required for temperature compensation. The interior of the cup is first dried by pumping desiccated air through it and the time then recorded for a measured rise in humidity resulting from transpiration through the leaf surface.

The figure shows only the leaf cup unit.

Stiles, W. (1970). A diffusive resistance porometer for field use. I Construction, *J. appl. Ecol.*, 7, 3, 617–22.

flow into a measuring vessel. An array of raingauges in the open and under the canopy is needed to make an assessment of the proportion of precipitation intercepted by foliage and directed down the stem, but because of the highly irregular pattern of drips falling from the foliage such an assessment can be approximate only.

SUMMARY OF CHAPTER 5

The plant contains two almost independent transport systems, the dead xylem vessels conducting water and dissolved nutrients upwards, and the living phloem sieve-tubes conducting metabolites downwards. There are interconnecting living medullary rays. Within the stele of perennial woody stems the old heartwood has no conducting function; it is structural and sometimes concerned with storage of water or metabolites.

The water conducting system comprises thin-walled living cells at each end of vessels consisting of thick-walled dead cells. The lower group of thin-walled cells, the outer layers of the ultimate roots and the root hairs, is in intimate contact with the soil water, while the upper group, the spongy parenchyma of the leaves, is in contact with the atmosphere via the stomata. Thus in effect there is a continuous column of water connecting the soil water and the atmosphere around the leaves.

The water conducting and water filled tissues have other functions also, including holding plant parts in their correct postures, expanding young tissues and producing mechanical movement.

CHAPTER 6

ENTRY OF WATER INTO THE PLANT

The movement of water around the hydrological cycle takes place in response to a series of merging potential gradients, the water moving because there is nothing to stop it; obviously at some point in the cycle a substantial quantity of energy must be injected and as we have seen this comes from the sun and is used almost entirely in the conversion of liquid water into vapour at the evaporating and transpiring surfaces of the soil and plant. All the rest of the movements including those now to be described take place because the potential at the lower end of each stage exceeds that at the other end, and so the water flows. Its movement up the plant depends on the water having sufficient cohesion to remain in intact columns in spite of the tension exerted by removal (evaporation) of water from their upper ends. This concept is therefore known as the cohesion-tension theory.

ENTRY OF WATER INTO THE ROOT

Transfer of water from the soil into the root takes place through the root hairs, through the relatively undifferentiated tissues near the root tip, and through the more or less suberised cells which form the cortex of most of the root system. Osmotic pressure within root cells normally exceeds that in the soil and hence water tends to enter, but it is generally considered that more water enters the root in response to pressure or potential gradient between the soil and the plant tissues than by osmotic uptake. It has been shown that the resistance of the cell cytoplasm to water flow is considerably greater than that of the cell walls and it is believed that much of the water passes through the cortex within the cell walls and so enters the xylem vessels directly.

Osmotic pressure of the external medium may sometimes exceed that of the cell contents. This can happen naturally, as in salt marshes, where indigenous plants such as the classic example of marram grass, have transpiration-reducing mechanisms to cope with the drought conditions induced by osmotic resistance to water uptake. More important in commercial crop production is the high osmotic stress induced by high application rates of inorganic fertilisers. Sporadic rainstorms and subsequent drying of the surface soil can cause violent fluctuation in osmotic potential in the surface soil. This is especially harmful to young seedlings which have not had time to develop root systems deep enough for some of the individual roots to be out of range of the intermittent osmotic drought near the surface. The same kind of stress may occur in arid regions where the whole water supply to cultivated plants must come from irrigation; here evaporation concentrates solutes in the surface soil and increases the osmotic stress to which the plants are subjected. Similarly in intensive glasshouse crop production, under conditions of concentrated and continuous feeding of nutrients, osmotic stress must be avoided by frequent watering, and by leaching out accumulated solutes by repeated flooding during the non-growing season.

As might be expected the region of most active water uptake is the root tip and the zone of root hairs immediately behind it. However, in a pine tree this region comprises less than ten per cent of the whole root system and although the conductivity rate through the cortex of suberised roots is only a tenth of that through unsuberised roots, it has been estimated that the mature roots absorb three quarters of the total water needs of the tree.

General resistance to water movement through the root cortex is usually considered to exceed that through the xylem vessels and so the rate of flow through the plant as a whole is mainly limited by root resistance, but circumstances can arise when resistances in other regions become limiting.

ROOT PRESSURE

If the stem of an actively transpiring plant is severed near ground level sap continues for some time to exude from the root side of the cut but not from the stem side. This exudation is said to demonstrate 'root pressure' resulting from osmotic uptake; certainly the osmotic pressure of the exudate is higher than that of the soil solution, but the rate of exudation is usually of the order of only 5 per cent of the transpiration demand. The absence of exudate from the stem side of the cut, in small plants, indicates that water movement upwards is continuing in response to the continuing gradient set up by water evaporating from the leaves. On the other hand, when an actively transpiring forest tree is felled, substantial quantities of liquid flow back through the severed bole. This is because the comparatively large diameter of the vessels allows air to move into them and simultaneously displace water; furthermore, the heartwood plays no part in upward transport of water (see page 71) and so air entering the cut heartwood column can bypass the waterfilled xylem vessels and rupture their water columns further up the trunk; additionally, because the heartwood vessels are not connected to transpiring tissue there is no water potential gradient up them, and so any water contained in them has no hindrance to its flowing out at the bottom.

That the phenomenon of root pressure has some connection with osmosis may be demonstrated by watering the soil surrounding the root

with a solution whose osmotic pressure exceeds that of the xyle̶
Root pressure then disappears, confirming that some part of the tiss̶
between the soil and the xylem vessels is acting as a semi-permeabl̶
membrane. However, if the mechanism were simple osmosis, the rate of
exudation from a de-topped plant would diminish as the xylem sap
became diluted with the water taken in; this does not happen and the root
pressure in de-topped plants can be maintained for long periods.
Furthermore root pressure is reduced by injection of toxins and by
imposition of anaerobic conditions; these facts suggest that some living
mechanism is involved and it has been postulated that the concentration of
the xylem sap, and hence root pressure, is maintained by transfer of sugars
into the xylem from living root cells.

Although root pressures of several atmospheres are commonly
recorded these are quite insufficient to account for the transport of water
to the tops of trees, and indeed in conifers, among which are the tallest of
all trees, it is difficult to demonstrate any root pressure at all. The
mechanism of the transpiration stream is discussed in chapter 7.

SUPPLY OF WATER TO THE ROOT

The passive movement of water into roots in response to the transpiration
demand of the foliage denudes the soil of water in the immediate vicinity
of individual rootlets, and of the rhizosphere generally; it decreases the soil
water potential. This automatically sets up a gradient which initiates a
flow from the surrounding soil towards the root system. There is
substantial resistance to this flow which increases sharply as the soil
moisture content falls (see page 67); thus there is a tendency for water
stress to arise at a rate which increases with increasing transpiration
demand. Soil water stress can vary between regions of the root system
located in different soil horizons which may have different moisture
retention characteristics; furthermore sporadic showers insufficient to
rewet the whole profile, will also result in a heterogeneous moisture status
in the rhizosphere.

The nature of the system is such that water flows into the roots
preferentially in those regions which are in the wettest soil, so that the
system tends to be self-equilibrating. Experiments have been performed in
which different portions of the root system are rewetted either with plain
water or with nutrient solution; a herbaceous plant such as lettuce was
able to obtain its full nutrient and water requirements from only part of
its root system so long as the transpiration demand was moderate, as in
dull weather. When exposed to bright sunshine and high transpiration
demand it could obtain its full requirements only when the whole root
system was supplied with water and nutrients.

⅃OTS TOWARDS WATER

...te that roots may be hydrotropic and geotropic but
either of these tropisms control growth and
field is debatable. In experiments designed to
the responses of different zones of the same root
..em with vertical barriers of soft wax, it was observed
incidentally that actively growing roots would sometimes penetrate the
barrier horizontally; they were unaffected by geotropism and were also
growing *away* from the wet soil into the non-wet wax. On the other hand
there can be no doubt about the proliferation of tree roots in a wet
environment once they have penetrated inside land drain tiles.

It can be shown that under experimental conditions in uniformly wet
sand, root proliferation and extension of the rhizosphere proceeds in an
orderly manner which is readily expressible in simple mathematical terms,
similar to compound interest growth. In glasshouse lettuce culture a single
watering at the beginning of cold-season crop life is sufficient to bring the
plants to maturity; they can extend their root systems fast enough to
exploit untapped soil and meet their full water requirements without
replenishment from outside. On the other hand, with the warm-season
crop which is subject to higher evaporating conditions, watering during
growth is necessary to avoid water stress. It is evident that the root system
is more than large enough to meet the moderate transpiration demand
during the cold weather, but only just big enough to meet the higher
demand during hot weather. It is significant that during the cold weather
the plants grew a bigger root system than actually necessary; the size of
the root system was not dictated by current demand.

THE EXPLOITATION OF SOIL AVAILABLE WATER

The soil is like a water tank of finite capacity; at field capacity the tank is
full, at saturation it is overflowing, while at permanent wilting point it is
empty (in fact at permanent wilting point the soil still contains an
appreciable amount of water, but this can be extracted only by drastic
means such as heating, and cannot be extracted by plants for their
growth). Thus the numerical difference between the water content at field
capacity and that at wilting point represents the capacity of the soil
reservoir, its capacity to hold water extractable and usable by plants. But
this is the capacity, and not the water itself, so that it is obviously
necessary to fill the tank, to fill the soil reservoir, if full use is to be made
of the available water capacity of a particular soil when growing a crop.

Furthermore, uptake of water into the plants takes place almost
entirely through the roots so that to make use of the soil water, roots must
either be present in the particular zone where the water is held or the
water must move from that zone to the place where the roots are. As has

been discussed in chapter 4 movement of water in soil is comparatively slow and takes place at different rates in different soils. In a sand, water moves faster than in a loam, but in both the movement in response to potential gradients is comparatively slow. The most efficient means by which a plant can utilise the soil water is by having an extensive root system. Thus the *efficiency* of exploitation of soil available water depends on the size and rate of expansion of the root system rather than on the movement of water through the soil towards the roots.

There appears to be little difference in ability to take up water or nutrients wherever an individual root happens to be on the root system. The idea of 'feeding' roots and special roots for water uptake is a fallacy. In the ring-culture system tomato plants, for example, are grown in cylinders of compost placed on a substrate of wet ashes; high concentrations of nutrients are applied regularly to the compost in the cylinders, but osmotic stress on the plants is avoided by the proliferation of roots in the plain water in the ashes. Although the upper part of the root system is certainly taking up mainly nutrients while the lower part is taking up water the two parts of the root system are not physiologically different from one another and no harm results if nutrients are applied to the ashes and plain water to the compost. Ring culture has no fundamental advantage over conventional growing methods, but it does provide a highly efficient way of ensuring that the plants are always provided with ample supplies of nutrients and of water, and it therefore usually produces excellent results.

Roots tend to proliferate where there are local concentrations of water or nutrients. The growth of tree roots inside land drains has already been mentioned. In blackcurrant *(Ribes nigrum)* plantations roots proliferate in the damp surface soil immediately under the usual straw mulch; in tea plantations generous nitrogenous top dressing results in multiplication of roots in the surface soil. In soil in which farmyard manure has been incorporated roots may be found concentrated in lumps of the manure. Plants intended for transplanting into the field are often raised in peat or card containers or soil blocks all of which contain ample nutrients and water; if the field soil into which such plants are set, still in their containers according to normal practice, is not also rich in nutrients and water, the roots will tend to stay inside the containers instead of ranging out into the field soil.

Roots will not grow into dry soil, but appear to extend into wet soil irrespective of whether the root system is already large enough to supply the current needs of the plant. Experiments to check whether plants copiously supplied with water have shallower root systems than plants only sparingly watered have not always given consistent results (figure 6.1) possibly because high genetic variability in root conformation of the populations studied has overshadowed the potential of individuals to respond to environmental variation in water availability. Even well-watered

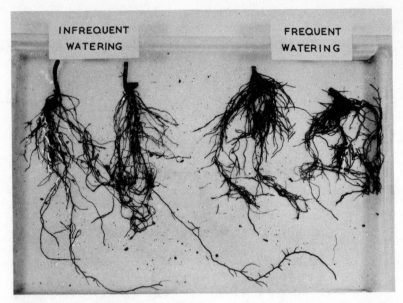

Figure 6.1 Root systems of broad bean plants grown with copious daily watering (right) and with less frequent watering (left).

plants produce some deep-ranging roots of unknown function (see page 73). The extent to which factors such as temperature, nutrient and water supply and transpiration demand control the extension of the root system is largely unknown.

There is evidence that failure of roots of tree seedlings to grow into dry soil was associated with the physical impedance of the hard dry soil to penetration by the comparatively soft root tips rather than with lack of water itself. Raising the physical pressure exerted by the medium on the outside of barley roots to only 0.5 bar (50 kN m^{-2}) reduced the range of penetration of the roots and markedly changed their conformation (figure 6.2).

In general any part of the root system takes up water in response to its local environment; if there is a local water potential gradient from the soil into the root, water moves in irrespective of conditions elsewhere in the root system. Thus in a root system dispersed in uniformly moist soil, water enters uniformly through all roots, creating a uniform soil moisture deficit pervading the whole rhizosphere. If there is now rain or irrigation and the amount of this exceeds the deficit, the whole rhizosphere is uniformly rewetted and the root system continues to take up water uniformly. If, as more often happens, precipitation is less than the amount of the deficit then only a portion of the soil extending from the surface downwards is restored to field capacity. The depth thus restored is directly

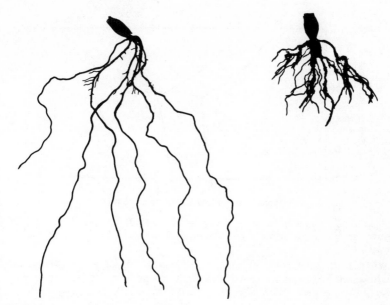

Figure 6.2 Barley root systems after 6 days growth in a medium consisting of 1 mm diameter glass beads, under atmospheric pressure (left) and under 0.5 bar pressure (right).

Photograph and data of M. J. Goss (1972) (private communication). Agricultural Research Council, Letcombe Laboratory, Wantage, Berkshire.

proportional to the amount of precipitation and the soil below this layer remains as dry as before (see chapter 4). The root system now takes water preferentially from the rewetted zone. Suppose a further shower now falls, smaller than the first; there will then be three different soil layers with differing moisture contents and so three zones of the root system taking water at three different rates. The system is self-compensating; most absorption takes place from the wettest soil so that conditions tend towards uniformity but in the field in a climate subject to sporadic rainfall throughout the growing season, the moisture status of the soil is heterogeneous; expressions of the overall moisture stress to which the plants are subject must be highly complex.

Before the advent of the neutron probe (see page 54) attempts were made to integrate the soil moisture potential influencing the different parts of the root system of a ryegrass sward throughout the growing season, by taking many thousands of soil samples for gravimetric moisture determination. The speed of operation and avoidance of soil destruction of the neutron moisture meter has made such studies commonplace (figure 6.3). Under irrigated conditions the soil moisture status is uniform provided that at each irrigation enough water is applied to restore the

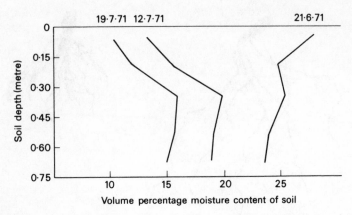

Figure 6.3 Changes in moisture content of coarse sandy loam (Wick series) under grass, during 28 days; measured with neutron moisture meter. See also figure 4.3.

whole root zone to field capacity. When this is done the plants can withstand evaporation up to the limit of performance of their root systems.

TEMPORARY WILTING

Under intense evaporative conditions transpiration demand can exceed the intake capacity of the root system even though the whole depth of ramified soil is fully supplied with water. This is a common occurrence in temperate climates, with such large leaved plants as sugar beet and brassicae. Temporary wilting ensues, often aptly called 'midday wilt', and this kind of wilting cannot be remedied by applying water to the soil. Indeed temporary wilting of plants growing in water culture can easily be induced in a dry laboratory atmosphere. Turgidity of temporarily wilted foliage can be restored only by reducing the evaporative intensity of the environment by shading to reduce incident radiation, or by spraying the foliage with mist to decrease temperature and increase air humidity.

MEASUREMENT OF ENTRY OF WATER INTO THE PLANT

Direct measurement of entry of water into roots is not feasible by simple means; it is usual to infer entry into a root system by studying changes in water status in different zones of the soil. This may be done quantitatively by repeated measurements of soil moisture made on samples, but such sampling destroys roots, and provides artificial channels for water redistribution. As an alternative, tensiometers (page 57) may be installed permanently at various depths and distances from the plant, or neutron probe (page 53) access tubes may be provided. Results of such a study are given in figure 4.3, page 64.

In water culture, uptake as distinct from transpiration loss may be measured by observing changes in the volume of the culture solution, but it is of course essential to prevent evaporation from the solution surface, for example, by means of an oil film.

DEMONSTRATION AND MEASUREMENT OF ROOT PRESSURE

A transparent tube is attached to the decapitated plant; the rate of exudation into the tube indicates the rate of movement of liquid from the root system up into the stem and so presumably also the current rate of water uptake from the soil. This technique may be used to collect exudate for analysis. A more sophisticated technique is to attach to the severed stem a mercury-filled U-tube manometer to measure the pressure set up as distinct from the volume of liquid transported. The tube connecting the cut stem with the manometer must be filled completely with water.

SUMMARY OF CHAPTER 6

Water moves towards the root system and enters the roots in response to water potential gradients initiated by evaporation from the wet cell surfaces in the leaves. Osmosis plays only a limited part in water uptake.

Although the fastest uptake occurs near root tips, this region comprises a small fraction of the root system's total absorbing surface and most of the plant water requirement is met by absorption through older partially suberised roots.

Resistance to water movement towards plants increases sharply as soil water content falls. The greatest resistance to water movement in the plant/soil system is probably at the point of passage from the soil through the root cortex.

Hydrotropy and geotropy are demonstrable but response of roots to these is not inflexible. Roots will proliferate into wet soil regions by growing upwards; roots will grow horizontally through non-wet media.

Water uptake by a root system is preferential in wetter regions and so the rhizosphere is self-equilibrating in respect of soil water content. Available water capacity describes the quantity of water which a soil can retain after excessive precipitation; available water can be exploited fully only if the root system ramifies the whole soil profile.

There is no distinction between water-absorbing roots and nutrient-absorbing roots; most roots can perform both functions virtually independently. The failure of roots to grow into dry soil is associated with mechanical impedance rather than the lack of water.

Temporary wilting ('midday stress') is the result of transpiration rate exceeding maximum intake capability of the root system. It cannot be alleviated by adding water to the soil but only by reducing transpiration rate.

CHAPTER 7

WATER WITHIN THE PLANT

We have seen that the plumbing system of the plant consists essentially of a more or less vertical column of parallel tubes dispersing into discrete branches at both ends (the xylem) and ending in close association with thin-walled cells (of the roots, and of the leaf mesophyll). The whole system is full of water. Commonly in trees the vertical distance between the extremeties of the tubes is many metres, equivalent to hydrostatic water pressure of the same height. To raise water to the top of an ordinary tree would require a pressure of 10 to 20 bars ($1-2$ MN m^{-2}), far more than recorded in the most successful of root pressure demonstrations. The rate of exudation from a detopped plant is usually only of the order of 5 per cent of the previous transpiration rate of the intact plant. Thus osmotic uptake of water into the roots cannot explain the flow of water to the tops of trees.

The flow takes place in response to a potential gradient set up by evaporation of water from the cells adjacent to the upper ends of the tubes, and is limited by resistances which differ in different parts of the plumbing system. These resistances are in relation to the lengths and diameters of individual vessels, the relative numbers of vessels, for instance in stems and petioles, and the interposition of transverse hindrances such as cell walls, protoplasm and the like, and, after the water has turned to vapour, the resistance set by the variable stomatal apertures.

TRANSPIRATION RATES

The maximum potential flow of water through the plant (potential transpiration rate) is determined primarily by the difference between the water potential at the root surfaces and that at the evaporating sites in the leaves; the actual rate is reduced in proportion to the resistances within the roots, stems and leaves. Measurement of these individual resistances is difficult but the magnitude of leaf resistance is probably of the same order as that of stem resistance and rather less than that of root resistance.

At night the water potential of the cell wall surfaces in contact with the air in the intercellular spaces equals that within the cells because almost no evaporation is taking place — the plant is not transpiring. There is then no upward movement of water in the xylem system and indeed there is a downward tension resulting from the pull of gravity on the stationary water columns. In daylight, evaporation from the cell walls

begins, a potential gradient is set up between the outside of the walls and
the cell contents which first results in loss of water from the tissues
themselves. Because the cell walls are elastic an initial change in size occurs
but there is eventually a potential difference between the cell interiors and
the upper ends of the xylem vessels. This sets up a similar difference
between upper and lower ends of the vessels and general upward
movement of water begins. There is now potential difference between the
lower ends of the vessels and the cells of the roots which accordingly lose
water; that part of their walls, including the root hairs, in contact with the
external soil water is then at lower potential than the soil water, and water
moves into the plant. Expressed crudely, water is sucked from the soil as if
the plant were a hollow straw, but one with controlling constrictions at
certain points.

The actual rate of transpiration varies irregularly as a result of
transient changes in the environment. There are also regular diurnal
changes in the water content of plants, which reaches a minimum in late
afternoon and a maximum during the night; these are at least partially
related to changes in transpiration rate. There are accompanying changes
in stem diameter even of woody tree trunks whose diameter is least during
the afternoon. As might be expected leaves show a similar rhythmic
shrinkage during the afternoon. Cyclic changes in transpiration rate of
much shorter periodicity than the diurnal changes have been observed in
sunflower, accompanied by changes in leaf temperature and stomatal
aperture. This inter-relationship could be explained by a 'hunting'
mechanism; if environmental conditions were such that potential
transpiration rate exceeded the capacity of the plant to meet it, stomata
would tend to close, transpiration rate and evaporative cooling rates to fall
and hence leaf temperature to rise. Reduction in transpiration rate would
increase leaf water potential, the stomata would open and thus a cyclic
series of events would be initiated†.

THE WATER STATUS OF PLANT TISSUES

The water within a plant is generally regarded as a continuum, that is to
say there is no barrier to its movement to or from any part of the plant
other than the resistances mentioned above.

Because there is a potential gradient from soil to air via the plant
tissues it follows that the water within the plant is always under some
tension or stress, but the term 'plant internal water stress' is quite
unrelated to the engineering term 'stress' which refers to deforming forces.
Plant water stress is derived from two distinct sources, osmotic stress
related to salt concentration in the soil, and simple water deficit resulting
from lack of water in the soil or high evaporative conditions around the
foliage.

The symptoms of internal water stress produced by these two sources

† data of Cox, E. F. (1968). Cyclic changes in transpiration of sunflower leaves in a
steady environment. *J. exp. Bot.* 19, 58, 167–75.

differ in that salt-induced stress manifests itself by thickening or darkening of green tissues, often with no wilting, whereas plain water induced deficit results in temporary or permanent wilting, reduction in growth rate, darkening in foliage colour and sometimes the intensification of a waxy bloom on the leaf surfaces.

WATER STRESS

Water stress is properly expressed in thermodynamic terms as the 'partial Gibbs free energy' or chemical potential of the water, usually shortened to 'water potential'. Other names have been used to mean the same thing, for example, diffusion pressure deficit (DPD), internal water deficit, capillary pressure or potential, suction pressure and total moisture stress. The water potential of a tissue within a plant is, like that of a soil, the sum of several contributing factors including vapour pressure (osmotic pressure) and hydraulic tension; it is expressed in bars or atmospheres.

The nature of water potential is best understood from the methods commonly used to measure it. Water potential may be measured in terms of the total water content of the tissues, or the energy status of that water. It is not sufficient merely to state the percentage water content of the sample; the water content must be referred to a standard such as the water content when the sample is fully turgid, holding its maximum possible amount of water. This parameter can be measured by weighing discs of tissue immediately after punching them from a leaf, floating them on water until fully turgid, reweighing, and then determining their dry weight. The water potential, or water deficit, or water saturation deficit of the original tissue can then be calculated relative to the amount of water in the fully turgid tissue. The term relative turgidity has been used for the relationship between actual turgidity of the tissue and the full turgidity of the floated discs.

An alternative method relies on the fact that when a tissue is not fully turgid, that is when its water potential is less than maximal, its cells will take water from any solution of higher potential and so increase in size. Samples of the tissue are placed in a graduated series of solutions of increasing salt content (and hence increasing osmotic pressure). The solution in which there is no change in dimensions or volume or weight of the sample has the same water potential. Conversely it can be observed which of the solutions themselves undergoes no change in density after the tissue sample has been soaked in it.

Water potential, or plant internal water deficit can also be assessed from associated changes in some easily measured physical property of the tissue such as the diameter of a stem, leaf thickness, or size of a fruit.

The overall water potential of an intact shoot resulting from summation of the potentials of its component tissues may be measured by enclosing the whole shoot in a chamber, with the cut end of the stem protruding. The gas pressure inside the chamber is then raised until water is forced back down the stem and appears as exudate from the cut end. The gas pressure on the outsides of the cells has counterbalanced their water potential and reversed the transpiration stream; the force needed to do this evidently equals the water potential. It may be described as the negative hydrostatic xylem sap pressure and can be of the order of 20–30 bars $(2–3\ MN\ m^{-2})$; the apparatus must be strong enough to withstand much higher pressures than this (figure 7.1).

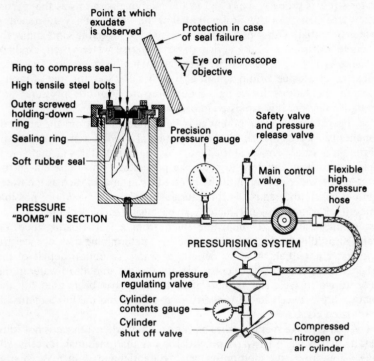

Figure 7.1 Apparatus for measuring total shoot water potential by flow reversal. The pressure inside the chamber containing the shoot is gradually increased by means of the main control valve, until sap begins to exude from the cut stem of the shoot. The pressure registered on the precision gauge is then assumed to equal shoot water potential.

This apparatus must be built, and tested, to withstand pressures up to 50 bars.

Scholander, P. F., *et al*, (1965). Sap pressure in vascular plants. *Science*, **148**, 339–46.

RESULTS OF REDUCTION IN PLANT WATER POTENTIAL

Effects on stomata

It is well known that the stomata of plants under moisture stress tend to close and there is substantial evidence that this constitutes the main regulating mechanism against excessive water loss. The mechanical functioning of stomata is well understood; the structure of the pair of guard cells is such that changes in their turgor change their shape and hence the size of the pore between them. The change in turgor is accompanied by a change in the concentration of starch granules inside them. Starch is not in solution and is therefore not contributing to osmotic pressure, and there is a reciprocal change in the sugar content of the cell sap and hence its water potential. Light causes starch to be converted to sugar and so opens stomata. One theory to explain this postulates that light favours the utilisation of CO_2 in forming sugar; removal of CO_2 makes conditions less acid and this in turn favours the breakdown of starch to sugar by the enzyme phosphorylase. Experiments in which CO_2 concentration within the leaf was artificially modified confirmed that high CO_2 caused stomatal closure while low CO_2 (less acid) conditions caused opening.

It is important to appreciate that gases can move through minute pores by diffusion; diffusion, which takes place by random motion of the molecules comprising the gas, can be a much more rapid process through small pores such as stomata than mass flow. If the pores in a membrane are close enough together diffusion proceeds almost as fast as if there were no membrane present. The distance between stomata on a leaf surface is often about ten times their diameter and at this spacing, when they are fully open, resistance of the leaf surface to diffusion is negligible.

All the water lost from a plant into the atmosphere passes through the stomata or the cuticle as vapour or, in a few plants, through hydathodes as liquid. Comparison of the relative amounts of stomatal and cuticular loss is obviously technically difficult; water loss comparisons have been made between intact leaves, leaves stripped of cuticle and leaves in daylight and in the dark, when the stomata are usually more or less closed. From these, it has been estimated that stomatal transpiration is between 3 and 150 times cuticular transpiration. Whatever the true figure, it is certain that most of the water passes through the stomata and that these therefore present means of controlling transpiration; they constitute effective hydrostats to control leaf internal water status even though there is still substantial cuticular loss when the stomata are tightly closed.

Many species have adaptations such as waxy coatings, hairs and rolled or folded leaves which reduce cuticular transpiration. In *Glycine* the hairs have been estimated to reduce transpiration by 40 per cent in moderate wind. Similarly it has been calculated that stomata sited in pits, as in *Agave*, lose water at only one-fifth the rate of those on a flat surface, even when fully open.

Gross physiological effects

Stomatal closure reduces not only movement of water outwards, but also movement of carbon dioxide inwards and this reduces the rate of photosynthesis. Gain in dry weight as a result of carbon assimilation is less in wilted tissue than in turgid tissue. Reduction in rate of protein synthesis has also been associated with decreased tissue water content; indeed the whole metabolism of the plant appears to be slowed by reduction in water potential, but though the resulting growth decrease is easily demonstrated the reasons why low water potential should interfere with the many processes contributing to growth are not known.

The connection between stomatal aperture, water loss and photosynthesis is aptly illustrated by the behaviour of the peculiar potato cultivar Droopy which is genetically unable to close its stomata. Hence it continues to lose water and wilts prematurely under conditions when other cultivars would maintain turgor by stomatal closure. Its leaves lose their proper posture for intercepting light and so photosynthesis and growth are reduced *even though the stomata remain wide open.*

Effects on growth and development

A lowering of plant water potential affects different organs in different ways. The commonest effect of moisture stress is a decreased rate of growth and development of foliage, and conversely, relief of stress causes increased foliage production. In sugar beet and grass stress relief induces a higher general growth rate than that of plants which have never been under stress, but the final yield of the relieved plants does not overtake that of the unstressed ones.

Lowered water potential at certain stages of growth has specific effects; an obvious example is the failure of seeds to germinate or seedlings to become established, but water stress at flowering of many contrasting species including peas, cereals and coffee influences yield of seeds. With peas water stress at petal fall and pod swelling stages affects, in some way not yet understood, the efficiency of fertilisation and subsequent growth so that fewer and smaller seeds are produced. The reader should consult the extensive literature on this subject (see bibilography).

One more important phenomenon so far not satisfactorily explained is that apical tissues and very young leaves appear to be better able to withstand the adverse effects of temporary low water potential than older tissues. In plants which have been subject to severe drought and then watered the old leaves die off and are replaced by the rapid expansion of younger leaves and the development of more young leaves at the apex. When the roots of transplants are damaged by bad transplanting technique and the plants are therefore subjected to temporary water stress, it is the older leaves which die off and the younger leaves which survive and eventually take over.

Transport

One function of the transpiration stream is to bring dissolved inorganic nutrients up from the roots to the sites of metabolic activity; this process ceases at night when there is little or no transpiration. Distribution of elaborated material and the products of photosynthesis in the opposite direction takes place largely in the sieve tubes of the phloem, but recall of these materials from storage tissues occurs both in the xylem and phloem. Low water potential interferes with both these processes.

MEASUREMENT OF FACTORS ASSOCIATED WITH MOVEMENT OF WATER WITHIN THE PLANT

Shoot water uptake

The uptake of water and hence transpiration, of a cut shoot can be demonstrated by attaching to the cut end a bubble potometer, consisting of a water filled horizontal capillary tube. The speed of movement of a bubble introduced at the distal end indicates the rate of water uptake. The cutting and attachment of the tube must be performed under water to prevent air entering the severed xylem vessels. Precise measurement of shoot water potential may be made with the pressure 'bomb' (see page 94).

Tissue water potential

The leaf-disc method has been described on page 93. There are several isopeistic† methods; a simple and effective one is to prepare a number of pairs of tubes containing a series of concentrations of a non-penetrating solute such as mannitol or carbowax in water. Samples of conveniently sized leaf-discs are soaked for a few hours in one of each pair of tubes; a drop of dye is then added to the other tube of each pair. Using a fine pipette some of the coloured solution is introduced below the surface of its pair in which the sample has been soaked. If the coloured solution rises the sample has taken up water and reduced the density of the original solution; its water potential is therefore higher than that of the solution. If the dyed solution sinks the leaf water potential was lower. Finding solutions of suitable concentration for a particular experiment can be time-consuming.

In the beta-ray method a leaf is interposed between a source of beta rays and a detector; attenuation of the rays is proportional to the mass of the leaf and is detected as a reduction in count rate. Changes in mass over a short period are almost entirely due to changes in water content; the method does not injure the tissues and can be used on intact plants in the field.

The water potential of any solution is related to the vapour pressure of the atmosphere in contact with it. This phenomenon is exploited in many methods for measuring tissue water potential. A sample is allowed to come into vapour equilibrium with the air in a small closed chamber; the vapour pressure of this air is then measured, for example by observing which of a series of solutions of different osmotic pressures, also enclosed in the capsule, does not change in volume. The solutions are conveniently

† Isopeistic means that the pressure is the same throughout the system; hence isopeistic methods for measuring leaf water potential depend on equalising osmotic pressure between samples and standards.

held in short lengths of capillary tubing. Alternatively the thermocouple psychrometer described on page 57 can be used to measure the vapour pressure of the enclosed air.

In the hanging drop method a pile of washer-shaped leaf discs is placed in a small airtight chamber immersed in a constant temperature bath. A fine capillary pipette is sealed into the lid of the capsule (figure 7.2). After equilibrating for about three hours a drop of water is partially extruded so that it hangs from the pipette nozzle; the drop is then withdrawn and its upper meniscus in the capillary is aligned with a reference mark. The position of its lower meniscus (and hence the volume

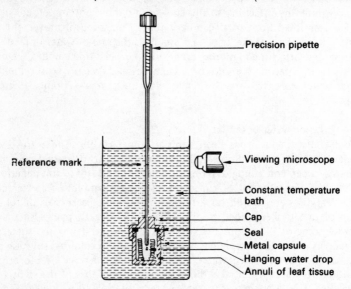

Figure 7.2 Principle of Macklon and Weatherley's (1965) hanging drop method for measuring leaf or soil water potential. For details of construction and operation the reader should refer to the original paper cited.

Macklon, A. E. S., and Weatherley, P. E. (1965). A vapour-pressure instrument for the measurement of leaf and soil water potential. *J. expl. Bot.* **16**, 47, 261–70.

of the drop) is noted. The drop is now extruded again for an exactly measured period of time, after which its volume is again measured. The loss by evaporation is related to the water potential of the leaf discs in the chamber. The apparatus is calibrated by exposing the drop to salt solutions of known water potential.

SUMMARY OF CHAPTER 7

Water within the plant forms a continuum, that is, there is continuous contact between the water present at the surfaces of the cells bounding the leaf intercellular spaces (virtually the atmosphere), the continuous columns of water within the xylem vessels, and the cortical cells of the roots and the root hairs. The walls of the external root cells are in contact with the water surrounding the soil particles. Hence removal of water by evaporation (transpiration) from the leaf cells sets up a potential gradient which is relayed down through the plant and out into the soil; water in the soil therefore tends to move upwards along this gradient.

The water potential of a tissue or a material such as soil expresses its ability to release water to a tissue or material at lower water potential, or higher water stress.

Reduction in plant water potential tends to close the stomata, which interferes with carbon dioxide inflow and hence with growth.

CHAPTER 8

MOVEMENT OF WATER OUT OF THE PLANT – SOIL SYSTEM

As has been pointed out, water moves round the hydrological cycle in response mainly to energy fed in at the point when liquid water is changed to vapour in the foliage or at the surface of the soil. By far the largest part of this energy enters as shortwave radiation from the sun. A comparatively small component comes in as advective energy, that is energy derived from a change in the temperature of the air as it passes over the evaporating or transpiring surface.

Evaporation can be measured, as opposed to being estimated, by means of lysimeters (see page 20) and evaporimeters (page 18) but because the adequate exposure of such instruments is difficult, estimates of evaporation from meteorological data are usually considered to be more accurate than direct measurements.

BOUNDARY LAYER

The boundary layer is the layer of the atmosphere adjacent to the soil surface, within which such parameters as vapour and heat flux change regularly and predictably with height. It is within this boundary layer that estimates of evaporation can be made with confidence. The boundary layer is disturbed by discontinuities in vegetation or topography and this implies that the point of measurement or estimation must be in the centre of a uniform area. For the boundary layer to be half a metre high requires a surround, or 'fetch', of uniform vegetation or soil some 70 m in diameter; a 2 m boundary layer theoretically demands a 'fetch' of 400 m radius. These conditions rarely occur in practice and the conclusion is inevitable that few lysimeters comply with these stringent siting requirements, and so their results must be suspect, and that meteorological estimates are applicable with accuracy only to broad tracts of uniform vegetation.

EMPIRICAL DETERMINATIONS OF EVAPORATION

It is comparatively easy to make rough estimates and rough measurements which are 'near enough' for practical purposes; examples of such empirical methods include the use of evaporimeters and evaporation tanks (see figure 1.9, page 17) and the direct correlation of radiation or of air temperature with evaporation. The radiation/evaporation correlation method has been used successfully in glasshouses. The best results are obtained by using a net radiometer or an integrating incident radiation meter instead of estimating radiation from sun-hours records.

The most widely used of the temperature/evaporation correlation methods are those of Thornthwaite and of Blaney and Criddle (see bibliography). The former is based on observations of mean temperature, which is strongly correlated with incident radiation; the method is better suited to large tracts of land than to small areas. The Blaney and Criddle method includes weighting factors to relate the estimate to local conditions; these must be determined afresh for each location and crop.

ESTIMATION OF EVAPORATION FROM PHYSICAL MEASUREMENTS

Because evaporation is a well-understood physical phenomenon its rate can be estimated in a basically straightforward, but in practice rather complex, manner from values of all the parameters which make up the physical environment including air temperature, humidity and movement, radiation, and the physical properties of air, soil and water. Soundly-based methods may be classified as energy partition methods, aerodynamic methods, and combination methods. Once the potential evaporation has been computed, actual evaporation and transpiration is derived from consideration of the plant species involved, the proportion of the soil shaded by foliage, the rooting depth and the type and moisture status of the soil in which the plants are growing.

Energy partition or energy balance methods

Of the sun's energy arriving in the earth's atmosphere a portion is reflected back into space from the upper surface of the clouds, a portion is reflected from the earth and its foliage blanket, and a portion is absorbed by plant tissues and the soil. This latter portion comprises the net radiation and can be measured as the difference in readings of two directional radiometers, one facing upwards and the other downwards. Incidentally with thermopile radiometers it is possible to connect them electrically in oppposition so that subtraction is made automatically and the current measured is directly proportional to the net radiation.

Most of the net radiation is consumed as heat of vapourisation of water in bringing about evaporation and transpiration; the remainder is sensible heat conducted either into the ground or back into the atmosphere where it warms the soil or air respectively. The heat conducted into the ground can be measured with a heat flux plate or it can be estimated from changes in soil temperature measured with thermometers, thermopiles, thermocouples or thermistors. The heat conducted and the water evaporated into the air can each be expressed in terms of change in air temperature and humidity with height.

Thus estimation of evaporation by the energy partition method can be performed by measuring net radiation, soil heat dissipation, and air temperature and humidity at two heights. The necessary instrumentation is sophisticated and interpretation of results is complex.

Aerodynamic or eddy correlation methods
These methods seek to determine directly the upward flux of water vapour from the crop—soil surface, in other words the evaporation rate. This involves measuring the vertical movement of air, and its water content. Although aerodynamic methods are attractive in that they measure directly the parameter of interest, their practical implementation is limited by their requirement for rapid response and highly accurate vertical anemometers and temperature and humidity sensors.

Combination methods
As their name implies, these methods combine the two concepts, the

Figure 8.1 Meteorological instruments required for making the Penman estimate of evaporation namely run-of-wind recorder (top left), sun-hours recorder (top right), maximum and minimum thermometers in Stevenson screen (bottom left) and wet and dry bulb thermometers to measure humidity (bottom right); notice the raingauge and evaporation tank in the left background.

energy balance pertaining to the air—plant—soil system, and the aerodynamic factors which influence transport of heat and water vapour away from that system. Combination methods first estimate the amount of energy available for evaporation, and then how the potential evaporation is modified by removal of water vapour from the system.

Potential evaporation can be expressed as loss from a theoretical unrestricted open water surface, or as transpiration from a crop—soil system; the necessary conversion factors can be derived from empirical experiments or by further mathematics based on pure physics. Because of the technical difficulty of performing crop experiments whose results are universally applicable, the mathematical and physical approach is usually regarded as yielding more accurate data than the biological experimental approach. On the other hand simple irrigation experiments can yield results which are applicable to local conditions; the temptation to apply them to different conditions elsewhere must be resisted.

Penman's formula

The most widely used combination method is that of Penman, which has distinct advantages over others. For agricultural purposes it can be applied using data derived from relatively simple instruments, namely sun-hours and run-of-wind recorders, maximum and minimum thermometers, and raingauge (figure 8.1). The estimate is considerably improved by using a recording radiometer instead of a sun-hours recorder.

Penman's basic formula is

$$E_T = \frac{\dfrac{\Delta}{\lambda} H_T + E_a}{\dfrac{\Delta}{\lambda} + 1}$$

where E_T is the potential transpiration rate
        Δ is the relationship between water vapour pressure and temperature
        λ is a constant related to air temperature
       H_T is the heat budget — the quantity of radiation available for evaporation
       E_a is a factor depending on air speed and vapour pressure — the drying power of the air

An abridged description of the principles underlying the derivation of this formula is given in the appendix.

POTENTIAL AND ACTUAL TRANSPIRATION

Whether estimated or measured, the result appears as evaporation from an open water surface, or directly as potential transpiration. Evaporation from an open water surface is usually greater than transpiration from a crop under similar exposure because of the intervention of resistances to vapour movement, such as imposed by reduction in stomatal aperture and the low permeability of leaf cuticle. In some instances transpiration in excess of open water evaporation has been measured. This may be due partly to the horizontal movement of air through the canopy and hence the introduction and utilisation of advective energy which would not be intercepted by the water surface, and partly to the efficiency of the highly divided and dispersed evaporating system presented by the foliage in contrast to a plane horizontal water surface.

The ratio of actual to potential transpiration may be measured experimentally, for example by using weighable lysimeters to measure the actual rate of loss from a confined plant/soil system for comparison with the estimate, and with the measured loss from evaporimeters. However, conditions in all lysimeters are inherently artificial in that the plant root system is confined and not permitted to forage freely for water. Furthermore the soil is isolated from the subsoil and so not subject to the same tensions and drainage phenomena as in unconfined soil. In attempts to circumvent this disadvantage lysimeters have been fitted with suction devices to equate soil water potential inside and outside the tank.

Most of the methods described, including that of Penman, yield estimates of transpiration from a green crop fully and uniformly covering the soil and with unlimited water supply. In practice crops do not always cover the ground; there is bare soil between annual row crops for 80 per cent of their field life. Furthermore as pointed out in previous chapters, reduction in soil water potential is a usual accompaniment of normal plant life.

ROOT CONSTANT, OR CROP CONSTANT

The volume of water which can be removed from a soil, before attenuation of the reserves begins to limit transpiration and evaporation, depends upon the soil texture and depth, its original moisture status, and the rooting depth of the crop.

The root constant is defined as the maximum soil moisture deficit which can be built up without checking transpiration. The root constant is primarily, but not entirely, a plant characteristic and it changes with growth and development of the plant and its depth and density of rooting. The root constant is expressed in the same terms as precipitation, namely the depth to which the quantity of water under consideration would uniformly cover the soil surface. For permanent pasture it is of the order of 75 − 125 mm; for herbaceous crops on retentive loam about 50 mm, while for fruit trees with deep root systems it may be over 200 mm. It must be emphasised that these are merely examples, the root constant of a relatively drought resistant crop like lucerne can exceed 100 mm whereas that for fruit trees whose roots are confined to the surface layers of a shallow unretentive soil may be less than 75 mm.

INCOMPLETE CROP COVER

Where there are bare patches between the plants and where the surface of the soil in these patches is damp they will lose water by evaporation at the same rate as an open water surface and hence little or no modification of the estimated overall water loss is required (here the difference between transpiration rate and open water evaporation rate is ignored). But if the bare soil surface becomes dry it will then lose virtually no water by evaporation and in these circumstances the calculated volume of water lost from the crop must be reduced in proportion to the area devoid of foliage. This is the principle underlying the traditional practice of conserving soil water by maintaining a 'dust mulch'. When applying this technique, cultivation to produce the mulch must be confined to the smallest practicable depth, otherwise damp soil brought up to the surface will lose its water and the net result will be water wastage and not conservation. It is easy to observe the water-retaining property of a dry soil surface in late spring, when moist soil can be found a few centimetres below the dry surface; this soil will remain moist late into the summer providing that no crop is grown and cultivation is avoided.

SOIL MOISTURE DEFICIT

As has been indicated, water moves out of the plant and out of the soil surface at a rate depending mainly upon meteorological conditions. The soil of the rhizosphere contains a finite quantity of water, reduction of which can be replaced by precipitation from above, by sideways movement in mass flow through fissures, or very slowly indeed by sideways and upward movement on a capillary scale in response to water potential gradients. This flux of water within the soil is termed redistribution, and it is a continuous process in soil in which plants are growing. In a normal season, other than in monsoon conditions, the rate of water loss from the system considerably exceeds the replenishment rate from these sources and hence the soil moisture content and the associated water potential is progressively lowered and a soil moisture deficit results.

The soil moisture deficit is the amount by which the current soil moisture status falls short of field capacity. It is usually expressed in precipitation terms and hence the deficit equals the maximum amount of precipitation or irrigation which the soil can currently absorb without drainage occurring.

DEPLETION OF AVAILABLE WATER

Soil moisture deficit is unrelated to soil type; given meteorological conditions will produce the same deficit on a sandy soil as on a retentive soil, but the effect of this identical deficit on crop growth will be very different in the two soils (see figure 3.6, page 45). For instance 25 mm deficit may represent depletion of most of the available water in the top 400 mm of a sand, whereas in a loam only half the available water will have been lost. Thus a parameter better related to the conditions to which the crop is subject is percentage depletion of available water. This is often used as a criterion to determine when to water in irrigation experiments. It will be appreciated that a given depletion of available water corresponds approximately to the same soil water potential in any soil, but it arises as a result of the loss of different amounts of water in different soils and the accumulation of different soil moisture deficits.

THE SIGNIFICANCE OF TRANSPIRATION

It has been pointed out that transpiration is a passive process which happens as a direct result of shortwave radiation falling daily upon a structure which consists mainly of water and which has a more or less permeable surface; loss of water at the upper end of this water-filled structure sets up a potential gradient which induces upward movement of water within it and hence a reduction in potential at the lower end, relative to that in the surrounding soil. Thus water enters and moves upwards within the plant as a transpiration stream throughout the hours of daylight. The transpiration stream has a transport function which could undoubtedly be satisfied by the movement of a much smaller volume of water, while the amount of water actually built into tissues is negligibly small. The transpiration stream is the source of water for maintenance of turgidity and posture, but this demands entry into the plant of no more water than the volume of the tissues to be rendered turgid. Evaporation of water from the transpiring surfaces keeps them cool by utilising, and thus neutralising, incident radiation which would otherwise heat the tissues; the transpiration stream is the source of this cooling water, but although its effect is significant its importance should not be over emphasised, for plants adapted to arid conditions survive without overheating in spite of having a very low transpiration rate. The fact that such cacti and succulents grow very slowly notwithstanding their exposure to generous supplies of radiation, which might be used for photosynthesis, indicates the most important function of the transpiration stream, which in effect is almost incidental. High turgidity holds the stomata open, permitting not only maximum throughput of water vapour, but also maximum rate of ingress of carbon dioxide for photosynthesis.

The growth of the plant depends upon uptake of carbon dioxide and exposure to sufficient shortwave radiation to photosynthesise this into carbohydrate; as a side-effect the shortwave radiation also evaporates large quantities of water which must be replaced if carbon dioxide ingress is not to be impeded by stomatal closure. This is the reason for the close relationship between growth and water supply postulated in the first sentence of this book.

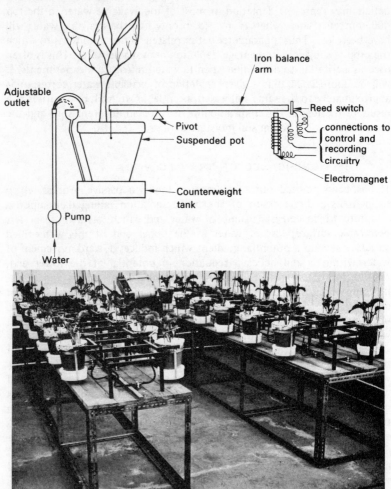

Figure 8.2   Principle of Cox's (1971) automatic recording transpiration balance. A motor-driven potentiometer increases the current flowing in the electromagnet until the balance arm is pulled down; the motion operates the magnetic reed switch which initiates recording of the over-balancing current (hence pot weight) and restarting the cycle. Should the pot have lost so much weight that the system fails to reset, the pump adds a predetermined volume of water either to the pot or for dry treatments, to the isolated counterweight tank.

   For constructional details and circuitry see the paper cited.

   Below — battery of twenty-four such balances.

Cox, E. F. (1971) Multiunit automatic recording and watering transpiration balance. *Rept. natl. Veg. Res. Sta. for 1970*, 90.

MEASUREMENT OF TRANSPIRATION

As stated earlier in this chapter direct measurement of the water vapour flux out of a plant, though possible, requires sophisticated apparatus. On the other hand inferential methods depending upon weight change of the whole plant/soil unit or plant/water culture require no more than a sensitive balance; these methods justifiably assume that weight change due to photosynthesis is negligible in comparison with weight change due to transpiration. Machines capable of weighing accurately substantial volumes of soil are expensive; hence the development of novel weighing systems for the lysimeters described on page 20. For glasshouse and laboratory cultures in small containers suitable conventional balances are adequate, but the extensive replication required to cope with variable plant material has stimulated interest in low-cost weighing systems such as the electromagnetic recording transpiration balance shown in figure 8.2.

MEASUREMENT AND ESTIMATION OF SOIL MOISTURE DEFICIT

Measurement of soil moisture deficit involves summation of soil water content in each horizon throughout the profile using bulk density determinations to express this on a volume basis. The total is then deducted from the total water content at field capacity (not the available water capacity). This is obviously a tedious procedure and it is better to estimate deficit using one of the methods based on meteorological observations of the evaporating power of the environment. The simplest method uses evaporation tanks and evaporimeters but satisfactory siting of all such instruments is difficult (see page 101).

Two variants of the author's deficit indicator comprising a combined raingauge and evaporimeter are shown in figure 8.3. These instruments must be sited in the crop to which they relate; they are sufficiently accurate for commercial irrigation.

A more accurate estimate of deficit is obtainable by using one of the methods for calculating evaporating potential by current weather parameters (see bibliography) but these require the use of properly sited and operated meteorological instruments.

Simple method for estimating current outdoor irrigation need

For countries with weather records extending over twenty years long-term averages of potential transpiration can be calculated. The factor causing by far the most variation from the average is, understandably, sunshine; thus it is possible to estimate current transpiration and hence deficit using only the long-term average transpiration, a raingauge and a sun-hours recorder. (In parts of the UK, the Agricultural Development and Advisory Service provides current sunshine corrections thus eliminating the need for individual growers to keep their own sun-hours recorders).

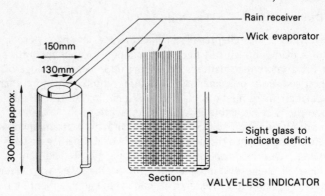

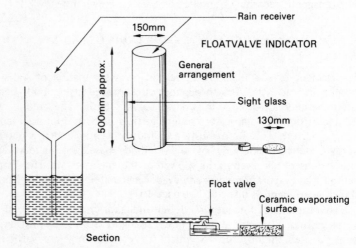

Figure 8.3 Irrigation indicators (soil moisture deficit indicators). Precipitation is stored in the receiver from which the wick or ceramic evaporator draws its supply. The instrument represents a plant growing in soil, and the water level in the receiver indicates approximately the deficit in the surrounding soil.

Winter, E. J. (1963). A valveless soil moisture deficit indicator. *J. agric. engng Res.* **8**, 252–5.
Stanhill, G. (1958). An irrigation gauge for commercial use in field and glasshouse practice. *J. agric. Engng Res.* **3**, 292–8.

The irrigator must keep an up-to-date balance sheet of his soil moisture status. Beginning about March when the soil is usually at field capacity (nil deficit) transpiration is subtracted and rainfall and irrigation added at weekly or fortnightly intervals. The transpiration figure is obtained from tables of averages plus or minus a weighted correction for the difference between actual and long-term average sun-hours per day. Precipitation in excess of the deficit will be lost by runoff or through drainage and so is *not* accumulated to offset future transpiration. On the other hand transpiration in excess of precipitation does accumulate and increases the deficit, which, if not eliminated by future rain or irrigation represents the maximum amount of irrigation which the soil can currently absorb without wastage.

Full details of this method and the necessary tables for UK are given in the Ministry of Agriculture Fisheries and Food Technical Bulletin 4 (Calculation of Irrigation Need) and its successor Bulletin 16 (Potential Transpiration), both by L. P. Smith (Meteorological Office) and published by H.M. Stationery Office, London.

SUMMARY OF CHAPTER 8

Water moves through the plant and out into the atmosphere as a result of the sun's energy evaporating water from the foliage.

Evaporation can be measured with weighing lysimeters and evaporimeters but because of siting and exposure difficulties it is usually more satisfactory to estimate these parameters from meteorological and other physical data.

Methods for estimating by energy partition or energy balance require measurements of net radiation, soil heat dissipation and changes in air temperature and humidity.

Aerodynamic or eddy correlation methods require direct measurements of the upward flux of water vapour in the atmosphere.

Combination methods, including the Penman method, combine the energy balance pertaining to the air/plant/soil system and factors influencing heat and water transfer away from that system.

Actual transpiration and evaporation is usually less than the estimated potential amount because of restrictions imposed by shortage of water in the soil, limitation of root range and incompleteness of cover of the soil surface by foliage.

The magnitude of the effect of a given soil moisture deficit depends upon the soil type and the percentage depletion of available water and hence the stress to which the crop is subjected. Usually the greater the stress, the greater the growth reduction by reason of interference with carbon dioxide uptake.

CHAPTER 9

HORTICULTURAL IMPLICATIONS

EFFECTS OF WATER STRESS ON CROP PLANTS

High soil moisture tension or stress (low soil water potential) caused by low soil moisture content hinders the passage of water into the plant and out through its transpiring surfaces into the atmosphere; the result of this hindrance is increase in suction pressure deficit within the plant tissues and this is intensified by high evaporating conditions — strong sunlight, high temperature, low humidity and fast air movement. These conditions are typical of the tropical and subtropical environment (and also of the temperate glasshouse) and need only the satisfying of the evaporation demand to transform them from being conditions almost lethal to plants to being conditions for maximum growth.

We have seen that restriction of water supply decreases carbon dioxide ingress and so a plant with limited water supply is smaller than one with unlimited water. Other effects are not so obvious. Organ development is often slower in water stressed plants, but there are exceptions such as the ripening of peas as evidenced by the conversion of sugar to starch in the developing seed cotyledons where relief of moisture stress as the seeds swell delays ripening and prolongs the period during which the peas are sweet enough to meet the requirements of the frozen pack industry.

The foliage of almost all water-stressed plants takes on a darker green colour than that of well-watered plants; the mechanism of this colour change has not yet been explained. In some waxy members of the Brassicae it is accompanied by intensification of the wax coating into a distinct bloom. Unfortunately by the time these features appear irreversible harm has already been done to the plants, and so they cannot be used as diagnostic criteria to decide when to irrigate.

The most obvious effect of growing almost any plant with unrestricted water supply is that it produces more foliage than when transpiration is occasionally limited; in nineteenth century gardeners' parlance, 'it runs to leaf' (figure 9.1). This extra foliage may or may not be accompanied by more or larger floral organs or storage organs (figure 9.2), and in this different species behave differently. The zonal pelargonium produces leaves in preference to flowers if over-watered but the cauliflower produces a bigger curd; the pea produces more peas per pod if extra water is applied just as the flowers are opening, but bigger peas if the watering takes place as the pods are swelling. There are response differences between cultivars; with copious water King Edward potatoes

114

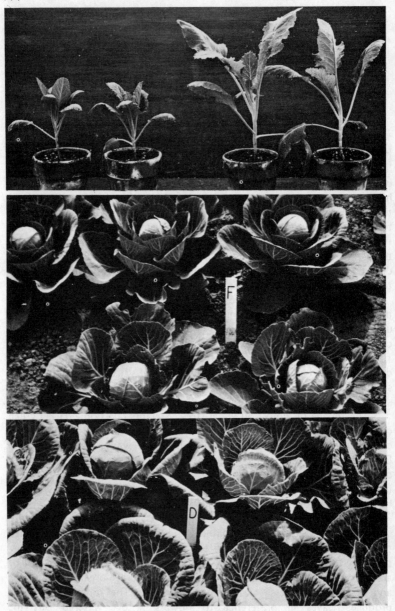

Figure 9.1 Above — cauliflower plants in pots watered weekly (left) and daily (right).
Below — cabbages grown in the field with rain only (F) and with daily irrigation (D).

Experiments of Mrs J. Steckel (1968). Private communication. National Vegetable Research Station, Wellesbourne, Warwickshire.

Figure 9.2 10 weeks old potato plants: 'wet' – watered daily; 'dry' – watered once weekly. Frequent watering has caused production of more foliage and more and smaller tubers (75 per plant, average weight 0.06 g) than infrequent watering (39 per plant, average weight 0.1 g). These are the numbers of tubers *initiated* and their weights at the time the photographs were taken; only a small proportion of them would have persisted to maturity under field conditions.

Data of Mrs J. Steckel, (1972). Private communication. National Vegetable Research Station, Wellesbourne, Warwickshire.

yield a profusion of small tubers, but Majestics give larger tubers with no increase in number. Some of these effects result from maintaining a particular watering treatment throughout crop life; others occur when moisture stress is relieved only temporarily at a moisture sensitive growth stage. One such stage has been mentioned for peas, and if this crop is watered *before* that stage the result is merely extra, unsaleable, foliage. Similar responses are known for grass, but here it is the foliage and not the seed which is the required produce. Thus the watering treatment which should be given to a crop depends upon which organs are to be sold.

LIMITED IRRIGATION

These phenomena provide an opportunity for making good use of restricted water supplies. For while there is no doubt that to obtain a maximum yield of almost any crop it should never be allowed to be short of water at any time during its life, in commercial practice this ideal can rarely be achieved. Shortage of water, labour or equipment can all result in periods of crop water stress. It is therefore important for the horticulturist to know the responses of his particular crop and to manipulate these to his best advantage in endeavouring to obtain maximum profit with minimum expenditure of water and labour. Maximum profit may well not be synonymous with maximum yield; under some circumstances maximum yield can be obtained if the crop is permitted to suffer water stress only between moisture sensitive stages, but in most cases this will result in yield reduction. What matters, however, is the profit in terms of return per unit of cash expended and this can be obtained by accepting a total yield less than the maximum but expending each litre of water in the way in which it will produce its maximum response. This usually means making the best use of natural precipitation and soil moisture reserves, and applying artificial irrigation only at known moisture sensitive growth stages. Table 9.1 shows examples of results obtained by such limited irrigation.

WATER STRESS AND PRODUCE QUALITY

Freedom from water stress induces fast growth rate and encourages foliage production, largely of crisp, tender non-fibrous material. In a crop to be eaten raw this is obviously advantageous. Freedom from stress also causes internal changes of a more subtle nature; the flavour of turnips becomes more bland, carrots and tomatoes become less sweet. The changes may or may not be desirable, according to the personal whim of the consumer. The foliage colour changes already mentioned may be accompanied by other colour changes, for instance carrot roots which become a darker red under water stress.

In a population freedom from water stress tends to make growth more even; this is probably the result of eliminating the effects of local

Table 9.1

Typical responses to limited irrigation; results obtained in field experiments

	Yield		Irrigation		Increase resulting from irrigation
	Rain only	Rain plus irrigation	Amount	Timing	
	t/ha	t/ha	mm		t/25mm/ha
Lettuce	15	19	30	soil restored to field capacity before sowing	3
Cabbage	41	59	25	3 weeks before cutting	18
Cauliflower	15	26	25	3 weeks before cutting	10
Early (i) potato	25	31	60	12 mm whenever soil deficit was 12 mm	2
(ii)	14	19	45	when tubers reached 8 mm diameter	3
Maincrop potato	37	50	100	25 mm whenever soil deficit was 50 mm	3
Self blanching celery	56	66	75	25 mm whenever soil deficit was 25 mm	3
Pea (i)	7	10	40	20 mm at flowering and 20 mm at pod-swelling	2
(ii)	12	16	25	at flowering	4
Carrot	30	34	60	60 mm when soil deficit was 75 mm	2
Apple †	22	30	270	1/3 of root volume restored to field capacity whenever tension at 300 mm depth was 200 mm mercury	2

Data of Irrigation Section, National Vegetable Research Station, Wellesbourne, Warwickshire.

† Data of Goode, J. E. and Hyrycz, K. J. (1964). The response of Laxton's Superb apple trees to different soil moisture conditions. *J. hort. Sci.* 39, 254—76.

differences in soil available water capacity; the produce also is more uniform, and may be fit for harvesting over a longer period.

Water stress and freedom from stress affect produce quality and flavour beneficially or adversely according to what is considered desirable in the marketable material.

WATER STRESS AND GROWTH

The level of water stress at which plant growth begins to be adversely affected is a matter of some controversy and many empirical experiments have been performed in attempts to determine this important value for particular crops. The diversity of local environmental conditions, including soil type, topography and most of all the weather during the experiment has produced a plethora of differing results. It is probably safe to assume that *any* reduction in soil moisture content below field capacity (or, more precisely, any decrease in soil water potential below one third of a bar) is likely to reduce growth rate below the potential maximum, and that the greater the permitted removal of available water, the greater will be the reduction in growth. Figure 9.3 shows that for one crop at least water stress relief follows the law of diminishing returns; the nearer the soil is to field capacity, the less is the response to 25 mm of irrigation.

Many results do not support this hypothesis; one reason may be the variability of the environment and the difficulty of repeating similar experimental conditions in successive years. This is an argument against carrying out a multiplicity of *ad hoc* field experiments in the hope of

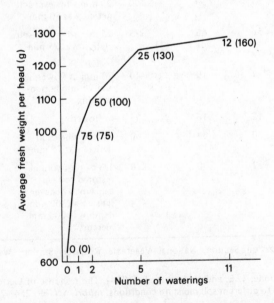

Figure 9.3 The response of cabbage to watering follows the law of diminishing returns. The figures at each point on the graph are the soil moisture deficit (mm) at which irrigation was performed, and, in parenthesis, the total quantity of water applied throughout the season.

Drawn from data of Drew, D. H., (1966). Irrigation studies on summer cabbage. *J. hort. Sci.*, **41**, 103–14.

solving problems of purely local interest, and in favour of studying fundamental principles governing plant—soil—water relationships under controlled conditions with the object of predicting likely response to a given watering treatment under any given set of local circumstances.

DEVELOPMENT OF WATER STRESS

The loss by evaporation or transpiration of a given amount of soil water results in the same soil moisture deficit whatever the soil texture, but the percentage depletion of available water by the same deficit differs in different soils, and it is this which influences growth. Available water capacity does not itself affect growth; it merely indicates the size of the soil reservoir, and the period for which the soil can support a crop in the absence of precipitation without build-up of harmful water stress. Poorly-retentive soils, that is those with low available water capacity, require watering more frequently than highly retentive soils. On the other hand, they release their water more readily than more retentive soils, and faster growth can be expected provided that the reservoir is frequently replenished.

MANIPULATING AVAILABLE WATER CAPACITY

In chapter 3 it was pointed out that available water capacity is a property related to soil texture, or particle size spectrum; thus the only way markedly to alter the available water capacity is to alter the particle size spectrum as, for example, by adding particles of an appropriate size. Addition of suitable ash, very fine sand or silt *of the required particle size* increases available water capacity in proportion to the quantity added (table 3.4, page 48). Certain waste products ostensibly suitable for this purpose contain phytotoxic substances and although it can be assumed that soluble materials will eventually be leached out of the soil, this merely means that they will be transferred as pollutants to aquifers or watercourses.

A less serious objection to this method of increasing available water capacity is the high cost of transporting these fine powders in special vehicles and of mixing them intimately with the topsoil. If such soil improvement were shown to be longlasting and worthwhile, no doubt these practical difficulties would be overcome.

A more immediately practicable method of temporarily increasing the water retention property of a soil is to incorporate in it large quantities of peat or other organic material whose function is merely to act as a sponge; this is the reason for incorporating organic material in glasshouse composts. Admixture of farmyard manure will temporarily increase the water-holding capacity of a field soil (table 3.5, page 49) but production of such manure with straw, dung and urine is no longer a part of modern farming practice. The slurry effluent from intensive animal production units, poultry houses and cattle yards has no beneficial effect on the water holding capacity of soil; indeed its only effect on the soil, apart from the very small nutritional benefit which could be more cheaply obtained from conventional fertilisers, is a harmful one on soil structure.

Attempts have been made to utilise cereal straw for soil improvement, by following the combine harvester with a chopping implement to enable the waste straw to be ploughed in instead of being burned, in the hope that there would be an effect on soil structure and hence water capacity. Ley farming, the interposition of one or more years of grass in the farm rotation, has a similar effect in temporarily increasing the available water capacity of the soil when the organic matter of the roots and the sward is ploughed in. It must be admitted, however, that although these practices do increase available water capacity to a measurable extent, the increase is hardly sufficient to account for the observed substantial yield increase which is usually attributed to improved root growth and function in the better-structured soil; this is probably a real effect, but is very difficult to measure.

Primary cultivation (that is, ploughing or discing) itself temporarily increases the available water capacity of a soil by increasing the proportion of voids to solid material, voids which can later be filled with water (table 9.2). This effect disappears as the season advances and the soil once more becomes compacted (see table 3.5, page 49). Judicious cultivation of horticultural soil is beneficial, but excessive cultivation is to be avoided because, as mentioned on page 67, evaporation ceases once the upper few centimetres of soil have dried out; over-enthusiastic cultivation brings up more moist soil to be dried out at the surface. Repeated deep cultivation

Table 9.2

Effects of different primary cultivations on the available water capacity of a sandy loam

	Available water ratio (see page 59)			
Soil depth	Shallow ploughing	Deep ploughing	Shallow ploughing plus subsoiling	Rotavating
0 − 0.15 m	0.067	0.068	0.083	0.094
0.15 − 0.3 m	0.068	0.081	0.078	0.064
0.3 − 0.45 m	0.054	0.079	0.074	0.076

Recalculated from data of Salter, P. J. and Haworth, F. (1961). Available water capacity of a sandy loam soil. II. Effects of farmyard manure and different primary cultivations. *J. Soil Sci.* **12**, 2.

can denude the whole profile of stored water; this is one argument in favour of chemical, as opposed to mechanical, control of weeds.

It is important to distinguish between structure and texture of a soil. Texture is a permanent property describing the size of the constituent particles. Structure is a temporary property describing the manner in which the particles are aggregated together, for example with transient additions of straw or organic matter of animal or vegetable origin; as this material rots, its effects on structure disappear and the soil becomes compacted. Structure can be developed by cautious cultivation, but it can also be destroyed by repeated cultivation, by application of water in excessive quantity or too large a drop size, and by long exposure to inclement weather.

WATER TABLES

So far we have considered the soil mainly in relation to water entering from the surface, but as explained in chapter 4 a limited amount of water can rise by capillarity from the water table and roots can penetrate to the phreatic interface (the region where the water table meets freely-draining soil). Thus when it is feasible, manipulation of the water table forms an important part of horticultural soil management. In regions of all-the-year-round rainfall, drains can be arranged to maintain a constant level to the water table, but in regions of seasonal rainfall it is necessary to be able, temporarily, to alter the drainage threshold so as to rewet the whole profile without permanently interfering with drainage and aeration during the cropping phase.

SOIL WATER CONSERVATION

The soil water should be regarded as a valuable asset in precisely the same terms as its nutrient content, its organic matter content, and indeed as the top-soil itself. Just as good husbandry implies avoiding the loss of top-soil by erosion and replacing nutrients removed by crops it also implies conserving precipitation by ensuring that the whole profile is fully replenished whenever opportunity offers, without prejudice to means of getting rid of excess water, while at the same time retaining the soil itself. In regions of sparse or severely seasonal rainfall, water harvesting is an essential part of good husbandry. One method of water harvesting is to provide contour bunds, or individual plant basins, so that all the precipitation is held on the soil long enough for percolation to take place, instead of its being lost by runoff; the same technique performs the equally important function of minimising erosion. Another method of water harvesting is practised where rainfall is insufficient to produce crops over the whole area and where topography permits collection of runoff from part of the land and its concentration on a smaller adjacent cropped area. Water harvesting of a different kind occurs in parts of Russia where there is little summer rain but substantial winter snow (see page 1). The melting snow saturates the surface soil before the water in deeper layers has melted and allowed the surplus to drain away. A crop is grown using this water stored in the profile, in the absence of sufficient summer rain.

EVAPORATION REDUCTION IN PRACTICE

The surest way to reduce water loss from plants and soil is to reduce the incident radiation. In the open this may be done by shading, as in tea propagation nurseries, or by sheltering the soil surface with trash, peat or straw, or with artificial films of plastic, bitumen or latex (figure 9.4). Living trees can be used to shade crops provided that species can be found whose roots tap a different level of the soil from that exploited by the crop. Shading with a non-living screen is usually prohibitively expensive except for high-value crops such as nursery stock or choice flowering plants. In glasshouses shading is commonly used allegedly to prevent undue temperature rise, but the plants are damaged not so much by the high temperature itself as by the accompanying excessive transpiration; frequent spraying of plants can enable them to withstand high environmental temperature.

Transpiration can be reduced by spraying the foliage with a solution which evaporates to leave an impermeable film. Such sprays are in routine use to prevent wilting of cuttings before they have produced root systems, but the stopping up of stomata, as pointed out before, prevents growth and this kind of antitranspirant is not suitable for crops required to grow rapidly. Antitranspirants which interfere with some metabolic process within the leaf without reducing photosynthesis have been sought, but so far with only moderate success.

A simple but effective means of reducing transpiration is used in traditional plant propagating techniques, namely the removal of some of the foliage of the cutting or transplant. For this technique to be most successful the lower, larger leaves should be removed; not only do these have the largest transpiring surfaces but the young leaves which are left are capable of expanding rapidly as soon as an adequate root system has been regenerated and so making better use of the available water supply.

EXPLOITATION OF THE SOIL RESERVOIR

A given volume of soil can contain a definite volume of water at field capacity; the evaporation and transpiration from the horizontal surface area that it presents to the atmosphere depend upon current weather. The water will be extracted through whatever vegetation is growing on the site; if there is only one plant fully covering the area, all the water will pass through that plant, but if there are several plants the water will be shared

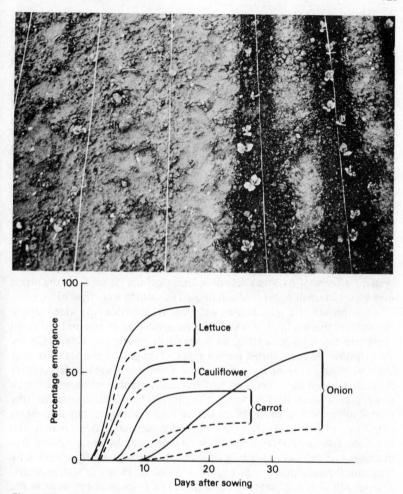

Figure 9.4 Above — general view of experiment to measure the effects of a film of bitumen emulsion sprayed over previously sown seed drills.
Below — effects on germination and establishment. Solid lines — bitumen-mulched; broken lines — unmulched controls.

Redrawn data of Sale, J. M. (1964). Effect of petroleum mulch on seedling emergence, soil moisture and soil temperature. *Exp. Hort.* 14, 43–52.

among them in proportion to their individual horizontal foliage areas. Thus for no other reason than that transpiration through each is less than that of the single plant, they will be smaller in size. But suppose that there are insufficient genetically small plants fully to cover the whole soil area; the original volume of water is now sufficient to meet the full need of each individual and each will grow to its full stature.

This provides a way for exploiting fully the soil moisture reservoir in the absence of any artificial irrigation. Wide spacing enables unirrigated plants to attain their maximum possible size under the particular environment; on the other hand, when irrigation is available the plants can be spaced more closely together and will still reach maximum size in spite of their combined transpiration demand exceeding the capacity of the soil reservoir to meet it. Irrigation provides the remainder. The advantage of irrigation in such circumstances is to enable more individual plants to be grown on a limited area; while this is pointless with a forage crop, for example, it increases saleable yield of crops in which the whole individual plant is the market unit, such as cauliflower, lettuce and radish.

GLASSHOUSE CROP IRRIGATION

For glasshouse crops the whole of the transpiration requirements must be met by artificial means. The plants may be grown in 'borders', with unlimited root run in natural soil, in troughs of limited but substantial volume, or in comparatively small pots or boxes. In some specialised systems a form of hydroponics, or solution culture, is used, or the plants may be set in small pockets of soil housed in soaking wet straw bales.

Equipment for glasshouse watering is available in wide variety throughout the world. The water may be applied as an intermittent aerial spray, by low-level sprinkling, by temporarily raising the water table, by subirrigation through buried porous pipes, from special nozzles on or near the soil (figure 9.5) or by capillary rise from a wet sand surface (figure 9.6). Because all the water is applied artificially glasshouse watering can be more precise than field watering. Usually the aim is to ensure that the plants suffer only a small deficit before each rewatering, but this entails risk from two sources. Overwatering under such conditions is only too easy; the risk of waterlogging can be circumvented by ensuring very free drainage, but this causes leaching of nutrients which is usually remedied by frequent replenishment with fertilisers dissolved in the irrigation water. The second risk is of infection and spread of pathogens and pests in the favourable environment of high temperature and humidity. Apart from elementary hygiene to prevent primary infection, with most glasshouse crops ventilation is needed to keep humidity below saturation and thus prevent water standing on the leaves.

Frequency of watering in glasshouses may be decided by using tensiometers or other sensors sunk in a typical part of the crop (see page 54), but under commercial conditions it is not easy to interpret the readings from only one or two instruments in terms of the whole house. The same applies to evaporimeters (see figure 1.11, page 18), but as these are usually cheaper than tensiometers it is possible to have more of them provided that the time can be spared to maintain them properly and collate the results. A better method of deciding when to water and how

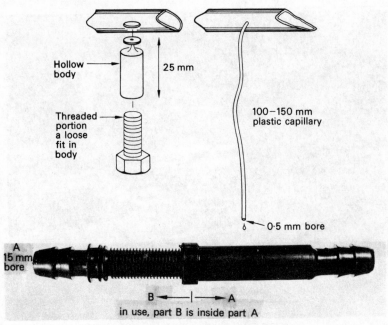

Hollow body

25 mm

Threaded portion a loose fit in body

100–150 mm plastic capillary

0·5 mm bore

A 15 mm bore

B ◄──┃──► A
in use, part B is inside part A

Figure 9.5 Examples of trickle irrigation equipment.
Top left – a metal or plastic hollow body buttons into a hole in the rubber supply line. A screw-like insert having a very loose thread fits into the body and water passes along the spiral channel formed by the looseness of the thread.
Top right – a length of capillary tubing is pushed into a small hole in the supply pipe.
Bottom – female part A has a smooth bore approximately 15 mm diameter. Male part B is also smooth bore but has a spiral groove on its outside, communicating with a delivery pore. This device, developed in Israel, is especially suitable for watering orchard trees.
   All these devices depend for their operation on passing the water through a long, high-friction channel and thus reducing its rate of flow to a trickle or drip.

much to apply is to use a version of the combination method (see page 103) to interpret local radiation data.

   One of the best methods for watering plants growing in containers in glasshouses is illustrated in figure 9.6. The containers are placed firmly in contact with a bed of wet sand which has a water table maintained a few centimetres below its surface. Water lost from each container by transpiration and evaporation is automatically and continuously replaced by capillary rise from the wet sand and so the growing medium remains permanently at field capacity. An added advantage of the system is that evaporation from the sand surface keeps the air humidity satisfactorily high around the plants. Such conditions are especially favourable for the growth of foliage, but where fruit or flowers are required it may be advantageous to induce moderate water stress on the plants by allowing the sand to dry out from time to time. Furthermore, with a crop such as

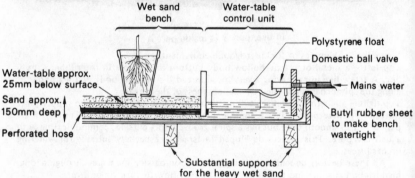

Figure 9.6   Above — capillary bench for automatic watering; notice the wide variety of containers. Each container has holes in its base through which the growing medium is in close contact with the wet sand, from which it takes water as required to maintain field capacity.
Below — principle of operation and constructional details.

tomato, continuous freedom from stress causes loss of flavour even though the appearance of the fruit is excellent.

Growing a crop on a capillary bench eliminates the need for assessing soil moisture status or evaporation intensity, for the containers take up only as much water as the environment has caused them to lose; the system is truly automatic. However, in autumn and winter when the glasshouse temperature and light intensity are usually lower than in summer, high humidity encourages the growth of fungi such as mildews and it is good practice to turn off the automatic water supply in the autumn and to rewet the sand only at infrequent intervals.

The roots of most plants growing on the wet sand bench stay within the containers but some, including Mimosa, several Brassicae, Fuchsia and ivy tend to range through the container holes into the wet sand. It is obviously better to prevent the formation of extensive external root systems in the sand by frequently shifting susceptible plants, than to move them only occasionally and so subject them to severe root pruning.

OUTDOOR IRRIGATION

Where there is little or no rain during the growing season problems of outdoor irrigation control are similar to those encountered under glass, except that there is unlikely to be sufficient water available to present any risk of overwatering. Where irrigation is used merely to supplement rain during the growing season there are risks of overwatering causing waterlogging, leaching of nutrients, and wasting of precious water.

Overwatering can be avoided by consciously applying no more than the current deficit and in countries where there is sporadic rainfall by applying *less* than the deficit thus leaving room in the soil reservoir for a shower of rain falling soon after irrigation.

The deficit can be computed by one of the methods described in chapter 8. At present the limiting deficit at which irrigation is deemed necessary can be decided only by local experimentation (but see page 104).

Outdoor irrigation may be performed by temporarily stopping drains so as to raise the water table, by flooding the whole surface of the soil, by flooding ditches alongside crop-bearing beds or by spraying or sprinkling water through the air onto the crop; with widely-spaced crops the water may be applied in basins formed in the soil around individual plants; for high value crops and for fruit trees a large-scale version of the glasshouse trickle equipment is used with one or two nozzles per plant. This particular system has the distinct advantage of wetting only a small area of soil immediately adjacent to the nozzle, and thus avoiding evaporative waste from most of the soil surface which is left dry (figure 9.5).

With the exception of these large-scale trickle nozzles there has been no major advance in the design of field irrigation equipment since the 1940s and the time is ripe for rethinking the whole problem of maintaining soil moisture potential at the optimum level for cropping. Designers are obsessed with the idea of imitating rainfall; they accept water wastage resulting from evaporation during the flight of the drops through the air, from wind blowing the drops away from the crop to be irrigated and from evaporation from wet soil and foliage; they accept that blowing water through the air requires power and pumps and precisely-made distributors and that to throw drops sufficiently far means that they must be of large size, and hence potentially damaging to soil structure.

Insufficient attention has been paid to the possibility of increasing soil water potential by some means operating directly in the rhizosphere itself, perhaps by supplying the water through porous underground pipes or channels formed in the subsoil, or by injecting silicones at a suitable depth to form a temporary perched water table within reach of the roots, or by increasing soil available water capacity so as to store more off-season flood water where it can be used, or, in regions of sporadic rainfall by making use of cultural practices designed to harvest every drop of precipitation and to minimise loss by runoff or evaporation.

WATER, SOIL AND THE PLANT

As pointed out in the introduction, plants cannot grow without water and they can grow well only in the presence of ample water, that is, in the absence of water stress. Obviously the provision of water for irrigation can render hitherto arid zones productive but usually only at high cost. Avoidance of all soil moisture stress can result in maximum yield under the prevailing conditions but the daily watering required for this is unlikely to be economic for any but high value luxury crops; it is more profitable to be content with moderate but certain yield, by judiciously supplementing natural water supplies only when these fall short. Irrigation coupled with extra fertilisers can produce spectacular results which may tempt the grower to indulge in over-watering. It is better to conserve natural water resources by water harvesting and erosion control, and by mulching to prevent evaporation wastage, and by minimising cultivation, and to regard artificial irrigation only as an insurance that the crop does not suffer stress at a critical growth stage.

Good husbandry implies manipulating existing resources of soil and climate, including water, to grow crops chosen to exploit the particular local resources in the most efficient and therefore the most profitable manner.

APPENDIX

DERIVATION OF PENMAN'S FORMULA

Penman's formula provides means for estimating evaporation and transpiration from comparatively simple weather measurements. The procedure involves estimating the proportion of the net available energy which is usable for evaporating water.

Of the total amount of shortwave radiation (R_1) arriving at the earth's surface, part (rR_1) is reflected (r being the reflection coefficient whose value for uniform green vegetation is 0.25), and part (R_B) is radiated back into the atmosphere as a result of the earth's surface having been warmed. Neither rR_1 nor R_B is available for evaporating water; the remainder, the net available energy or heat budget, is designated H

$$H = R_1 - rR_1 - R_B \tag{1}$$

The back radiation (R_B) is governed by atmospheric temperature, humidity and cloudiness

$$R_B = \sigma T_a^4 \, (0.47 - 0.075 \, e_d^{\frac{1}{2}}) \, (0.17 - 0.83 \, n/_N) \tag{2}$$

where

σ is Stephan's constant relating radiation to surface temperature

T_a is the air temperature in degrees K

e_d is the water vapour pressure at that temperature in mm mercury

$n/_N$ is the ratio of actual to possible hours of bright sunshine for the locality and date

Of the net available energy H, part Q is expended in warming the air immediately above the earth while the remainder E is used in the evaporation of water

$$H = Q + E \tag{3}$$

In the following equations the quantities are expressed in energy equivalents, using an unconventional unit of 59 calories per cm^2 which is the energy needed to evaporate 0.1 g of water or 1 mm depth over 1 cm^2.

The transfer of heat Q depends upon wind and the vertical temperature difference

$$Q = \gamma f(u) \, (T_s - T_a) \tag{4}$$

where

γ is a constant introduced to make all the units consistent
$f(u)$ is a function of wind speed
T_s is the temperature at the evaporating surface (soil, water or the cell walls within the leaf)

Evaporation rate E depends upon wind and the vertical vapour pressure difference

$$E = f_i(u)(e_s - e_d) \qquad (5)$$

where

e_s is the saturation water vapour pressure at temperature T_s
f_i is assumed to equal f for practical purposes

The drying capacity of the air E_a depends upon wind and the deficiency of the air water content below saturation

$$E_a = f(u)(e_a - e_d)$$

For a uniform grass sward this has been evaluated as

$$E_a = 0.35(e_a - e_d)(1 + u_2/100) \qquad (6)$$

where

e_a is the saturation water vapour pressure at mean air temperature in mm of mercury
u_2 is the wind speed at 2 miles height in miles per day

Penman used the slope Δ of the vapour pressure/temperature relationship to eliminate from these equations the parameters which were difficult to measure leaving only those which could readily be observed using simple meteorological instruments

$$\Delta = \frac{(e_s - e_a)}{(T_s - T_a)}$$

$$T_s - T_a = \frac{e_s - e_a}{\Delta}$$

substituting in equation 4

$$Q = \frac{\gamma f(u)(e_s - e_a)}{\Delta}$$

but from equation 3

$$Q = H - E$$

therefore

$$H - E = \frac{\gamma f(u)(e_s - e_a)}{\Delta}$$

$$\Delta/\gamma\,(H\ -\ E)\ =\ f(u)\,(e_s\ -\ e_a)$$

$(e_s\ -\ e_a)$ can be rewritten as $(e_s\ -\ e_d)\ -\ (e_a\ -\ e_d)$

then

$$\Delta/\gamma\,(H\ -\ E)\ =\ f(u)\,(e_s\ -\ e_d)\ -\ f(u)\,(e_a\ -\ e_d)$$

substituting from equations 5 and 6

$$\Delta/\gamma\,(H\ -\ E)\ =\ E\ -\ E_a$$

$$E\ =\ \frac{\Delta/\gamma\,H\ +\ E_a}{\Delta/\gamma\ +\ 1} \tag{7}$$

Thus evaporation rate E can be evaluated from determinations of the net available energy H and the drying capacity of the air E_a, modified by two physical entities Δ and γ. These have the same dimensions and so their ratio is simply a number, dependent upon temperature; its summer value is usually between 1.5 and 2.0

H can be determined from equations 1 and 2, E_a from equation 6, and hence equation 7 can be solved for E. The numerical values are obtained in the following ways:

R_1 measured with a radiometer or estimated from the ratio n/N
n measured with a sun-hours recorder
N from tables of latitude and date
T_a temperature of the air above the evaporating surface measured with a thermometer housed in a Stevenson screen
e_d vapour pressure of the air, from tables, using values measured with wet and dry bulb thermometers also housed in a Stevenson screen
e_a saturation vapour pressure at temperature T_a from tables
u wind speed, from 24 hours wind run measured with a cup anemometer
σ, γ and Δ from tables

Further information about the Penman concept and its application in research will be found in the series of papers, Woburn Irrigation I–IV, by H. L. Penman, *J. agric. Sci. Camb.*, (1962) **58** and (1970) **75**. A description of its application in commercial horticulture, a worked example and the necessary tables are given in M.A.F.F. Bulletin 16, *Potential transpiration*, by L. P. Smith (1967), H.M. Stationery Office.

The above account is condensed from these publications by kind permission of both authors.

BIBLIOGRAPHY

Most of the following publications were chosen because they give authoritative reviews with numerous references which enable a reader to pursue the required parts of a subject in detail. Considerable use has been made of Kozlowski's *Water deficits and plant growth*, which covers in only two volumes many of the subjects dealt with in elementary fashion in this book.

A few of the publications cited are papers chosen to expand or illustrate points made in the text.

CHAPTER 1 — THE WATER BALANCE

GREEN, F. W. H. (1970). Some isopleth maps based on lysimeter observations in the British Isles in 1965, 1966 and 1967. *J. Hydrol.* **10**, 127—40.
> An example of a method for using drainage lysimeters to estimate the monthly surplus or deficit of precipitation in relation to evaporation.

JENSEN, M. E. (1968). Water consumption by agricultural plants. In *Water deficits and plant growth*, Vol. II (Ed. Kozlowski, T.T.) Academic Press, London. pp. 1—22.
> A review of the factors influencing water consumption by crops, including climate, plant characteristics and soil water status; 66 references.

PENMAN, H. L. (1970). The water cycle. *Scient. Am.* **223**, 3, 98—107.
> An authoritative account of the dependance of man on water in the context of world agriculture.

CHAPTER 2 — WATER SUPPLIES FOR HORTICULTURE

ANON. (1967). Water for irrigation. *Bull. Minist. Agric. Fish Fd*, No. 202.
> Methods available to farmers for obtaining and measuring irrigation water supplies.

CARTER, R. W. *et al.* (1971). The use of weirs and flumes in stream gauging. *Tech. Note W.M.O. Geneva No. 117.*
> Working drawings, calibration methods, and mathematical theory underlying weir and flume design.

CHAPMAN, T. G. (1967). Measurements for water resource assessment. In *The collection and processing of field data* (Ed. Bradley, E. F. and Denmead, O. T.) Interscience, New York.
> Sophisticated methods for measuring the flow of large and small rivers.

CHAPTER 3 – THE SOIL RESERVOIR

GARDNER, W. R. (1968). Availability and measurement of soil water. In *Water deficits and plant growth, Vol. I* (Ed. Kozlowski, T.T.) Academic Press London. p. 107–35.

A review, with 45 references, of present knowledge of the energy relationships of water in soil, supported by mathematical interpretation.

NIELSEN, D. R. and BIGGAR, J. W. (1967). The physical characterisation of field soils. In *The collection and processing of field data* (Ed. Bradley, E. F. and Denmead, O. T.) Interscience, New York.

A review of methods of classifying soils and measuring their physical properties, including those relating to moisture.

CHAPTER 4 – MOVEMENT OF WATER IN SOIL

MOORE, F. D. (1970). Furrow irrigation of lettuce resulting in water and nitrogen loss. *J. Am. Soc. hort. Sci.* **95**, 471–74.

Description of an experiment illustrating the harmful effects of applying large quantities of water to a permeable soil in an arid region.

WESSELING, J. (1968). Hydrology, soil properties, crop growth and land drainage. *Tech. Bull. Inst. Ld. Wat. Mgmt. Res.*, No. 57.

The effects of excess water and of water table depth on crops, and methods of improving conditions by drainage; illustrated by mathematical treatment of the data.

CHAPTER 5 – THE HYDROLOGICAL STRUCTURE OF VASCULAR PLANTS

ESAU, K. (1959). *Anatomy of seed plants.* Wiley, New York.

A copiously illustrated detailed description of the microscopic structure of vascular plants.

CHAPTER 6 – ENTRY OF WATER INTO THE PLANT

NEWMAN, E. I. (1969). Water movement to plant roots. In *Techniques used in soil investigations* Rept Welsh Soils Discussion Group, University College of Wales, Aberystwyth, No. 10, 1–12.

Critical discussion, supported by mathematical argument, of the movement of water towards and into the root system.

CHAPTER 7 – WATER WITHIN THE PLANT

BARRS, H. D. (1968). Determination of water deficits in plant tissues. In *Water deficits and plant growth, Vol. I* (Ed. Kozlowski, T.T.) Academic Press, London. pp. 236–368.

Critical illustrated description of a very large number of methods (500 references) for measuring plant water content, total potential, osmotic potential, turgor pressure and stomatal aperture.

GATES, C. T. (1968). Water deficits and the growth of herbaceous plants. In *Water deficits and plant growth, Vol. II* (Ed. Kozlowski, T.T.) Academic Press, London. pp. 135–90.

A detailed review of current knowledge (103 references) on the effects of water stress on plant development and growth.

CHAPTER 8 — MOVEMENT OF WATER OUT OF THE PLANT—SOIL SYSTEM

HUDSON, J. P. (1968). Lysimeters and weighable containers in greenhouse experimentation. *Acta hortic.* 7, 104—14.
    A description, with practical details, of lysimetric methods for studying plant water use under glass.

STANHILL, G., BAIER, W., DOYLE, J. J., GANGAPADHAYA, M., RAZUMOVA, L. A. and WINTER, E. J. (1968). Practical soil moisture problems in agriculture. *Tech. Note W.M.O. Geneva*, No. 97.
    A review of world practice in estimating and measuring moisture status and the utilisation of water by crops.

TANNER, C. B. (1968). Evaporation of water from plants and soil. In *Water deficits and plant growth*, *Vol. I* Ed. Kozlowski, T.T.) Academic Press, London. pp. 74—106.
    A review couched mainly in mathematical terms, of methods of determining water use by vegetation.

CHAPTER 9 — HORTICULTURAL IMPLICATIONS

ANON. (1974). Irrigation. *Bull, Minist. Agric. Fish Fd*, No. 138, 4th edn.
    A comprehensive account of commercial irrigation practice in a temperate climate, in the open and under glass, including water supplies, soils, equipment, watering recommendations for most crops, and economic aspects.

ANON. (1970). Irrigation guide. *Sht Term Lflt Minist. Agric. Fish Fd*, No. 71.
    Practical instructions for commercial growers regarding the best commercial watering treatments for most UK crops.

LAVERTON, S. (1964). *Irrigation, its profitable use for agricultural and horticultural crops.* Oxford University Press, London.
    An account in lay terms of the theory, practice and economics of commercial irrigation in the UK.

PENMAN, H. L. (1963). Irrigation in Great Britain. *Jl. R. Soc. Arts*, 272—89.
    A lecture based largely on the author's own studies of the responses of agricultural crops to supplementary watering.

PIERRE, W. H., KIRKHAM, D., PESEK, J., and SHAW, R. (Eds.) (1966) *Plant environment and efficient water use.* American Society of Agronomy, Wisconsin.
    A collection of thirteen papers by leading American authorities on plant, soil, water and nutrient relations, including yield effects, water conservation, water use efficiency and likely future developments.

SALTER, P. J. and GOODE, J. E. (1967). Crop responses to water at different stages of growth. *Res. Rev. Commonw. Bur. Hort. Pl. Crops*, No. 2.
    A comprehensive review of world literature (1195 references) on the responses of tropical and temperate crops of all kinds to relief of moisture stress, and to temporary and prolonged drought.

TAYLOR, J. A. (1969). *The role of water in agriculture.* Pergamon, Oxford.
    Thirteen papers by UK authorities on precipitation, evaporation, water use in agriculture, irrigation and related subjects.

INDEX

acceptance rate of water by soil 8
actual evaporation 102
actual transpiration 104, 105
adventitious root 72
aerodynamic methods for estimating evaporation 103
Agave 95
Agropyron intermedium 41
almond 32
aloe 76
Alvim, P. de T. 77
anti-transpirant 122
apparent specific gravity 48, 50, 51
apple 31, 117
aquifer 1, 28
asparagus 31
automatic watering 125
available water 84, 85
available water capacity 38, 43, 59, 119
available water depletion 106, 107
azalea 31

Baier, W. 135
barley 86, 31
Barrs, H.D. 134
basin irrigation 127
bean, broad 72, 86
beet, red 31
      sugar 31, 88
beta ray method for measuring moisture content 97
Biggar, J.W. 134
bitumen emulsion 123
blackcurrant 85
Blaney, F. 102
Blundell, R. 7
borehole 26

boundary layer 101
Bradley, E.F. 133, 134
brassicae 127
bulk density 48, 50, 51
bituminous felt lining for reservoirs 26
butyl rubber 26

cabbage 31, 62, 114, 117, 118
cactus 23
capillary flow 66
capillary watering 126
capping 62
carnation 31
carrot 31, 116, 117, 123
Carter, R.W. 133
Cassia fasciculata 41
cauliflower 23, 31, 113, 114, 117, 123, 124
celery 30, 117
cereals 96
Chapman, T.G. 133
characteristic, of soil 40
characteristic measurement 56
Childs, E.C. 40
chrysanthemum 31
citrus 32
clematis 31
clover 31
cocksfoot grass 31
coffee 96
cohesion—tension theory 81
combination methods for estimating evaporation 103
combined evaporimeter and rain-gauge 19
consumptive water use 45
correlation methods for estimating evaporation 102
Cox, E.F. 92, 108
Criddle, W.D. 102

crop constant 105
crop cover 106
Crump weir 32
cultivation effect on soil available
    water capacity 49

daffodil 31
dam, cross-stream 25
deficit 7, 10, 18, 92, 109
Denmead, O.T. 133, 134
desalination 29
dew 8
dew gauge 15
dew point 9
diffusion 95
diffusion pressure deficit 93
drains, land 27
drainage 9, 10
drainage measurement 22, 68
drainage rate 43
Drew, D.H. 118
Droopy 96
drought 7
Doyle, J.J. 135

eddy correlation methods for
    estimating evaporation 103
energy-balance methods for esti-
    mating evaporation 102
energy-partition methods for esti-
    mating evaporation 102
erosion 61
erosion measurement 68
Esau, K. 134
estuarine barrage 29
evaporation 7, 8, 67, 101, 102
evaporation measurement 16
evaporation pan, USDA Class A
    17
evaporation reduction 122
evaporation tank, Russian 17
evaporation tank, UK 17
evaporation tanks 16
evaporative potential 16, 19
evaporimeter 18, 105, 124
    calibration of 19
evapo-transpiration 8

farmyard manure 119

field capacity 9, 42
    measurement of 58
    resin method for measuring
        58
field irrigation 127
flood irrigation 127
foliage 73
Forsgate, J.A. 21
French bean 31
frost 12
Fuchsia 127

Gangapadhaya, M. 135
Gardner, R.W. 134
Garnier, B.J. 21
Gates, C.T. 134
gauging station, river 32
geotropism 84
Gezira 18
gladiolus 31
glasshouse watering 124
Glycine 95
Goode, J.E. 117, 135
Goss, M.J. 87
grape 31
grass 7, 23, 31, 64, 116
Green, F.H.W. 133
ground-level raingauge 15

Hand, D.W. 21
hanging drop method 98
Haworth, F. 120
heartwood 82
heat flux plate 102
Helianthus annuus 41
Helxine soleirolii 45
hookgauge 17
horizon, soil 36
Hosegood, P.H. 21
Hudson, J.P. 18, 21, 135
hydathode 71, 73
hydraulic conductivity 64
hydraulic conductivity measure-
    ment 53, 69
hydraulic lysimeter 20
    20
hydrological cycle 1
hydroponics 124
hydrostatic potential 50
hydrotropism 84

hypocotyl 73
Hyrycz, K.J. 117

impeded drainage 66
India 1
indicator, irrigation 110
infiltration measurement 52, 77
infiltration rate 8
interception of rainfall 76
International System of soil
    classification 36, 38
irrigation 116
irrigation indicator 110
isohyet 10
isopeistic methods 97
Israel 18

Jensen, M.E. 133
Jones, D.A. 18

kale 31
Kenya 18
Khasi Mountains 8
Kirkham, D. 135
Koslowski, T.T. 133, 134, 135
Kubishevsk 1

land drains 27
lateral flow 64
Laverton, S. 135
leaching 9, 66
lenticel 71, 73
lettuce xiii, 23, 31, 62, 83, 84,
    117, 123, 124
Leyton, L. 76
licence for water abstraction 34
lining materials for reservoirs 26
lucerne 23, 31, 105
lysimeter 19, 20, 101, 105

Macklon, A.E.S. 98
maize (see also *Zea*) 31
mains, public water 26
mangold 31
marling 46
marram grass 81
mass flow 64
matric potential 50
matric suction 38, 50
meadow foxtail grass 31

mechanical analysis of soil 37
medullary ray 71
meteorological instruments 12,
    13
Mimosa 76, 127
MIT (Massachusetts Institute of
    Technology) system of soil
    classification 36
moisture release characteristic
    curve 40
moisture sensitive growth stage
    116
Moore, F.D. 134
Moore, R.A. 17
Morecambe Bay 29
movement of plant parts 76
McCulloch, J.S.G. 21

Nasturtium 73
Neilsen, D.R. 134
net radiation 102
neutron probe 53, 54
Newman, E.I. 134
Nicotiana attenuata 41

onion 31, 123
organic irrigation 30
osmotic suction 38

pan, soil 66
pea 23, 31, 96, 113, 116, 117
Pelargonium 72, 113
Peltier effect 57
Penman, H.L. 103, 129, 131,
    133
Penman formula 104
permanent wilting point 41, 58
permeability 53, 69
Pesek, J. 135
pF 39
phloem 73
photosynthesis 96
Piché evaporimeter 18, 19
Pierre, W.H. 135
pine 82
pit rain gauge 15
plant internal water stress 92
plant water potential 94, 95
plum 31

pollution 29
polyethylene ('polythene') reservoir lining sheet 26
polyvinyl chloride (PVC) reservoir lining sheet 26
Popov, O.V. 21
pore space 37
porometer 77
potato 31, 72, 96, 113, 115, 117
potential evaporation 102
potential gradient 91, 92
potential soil water 37
potential transpiration 104, 105
potometer 97
pound, offstream 25
precipitation 1
precipitation distribution 1
precipitation measurement 13
precipitation rate 8
pressure bomb 94
pressure membrane apparatus 56
pulverised fuel ash (PFA) 46, 48, 119
pulvinus 76
pumping machinery 24

quality of produce 116

radiometer 102
radish 63, 124
rainfall distribution 1
rain gauge 13, 14, 15
rain shadow 15
raspberry 31
Rasumova, L.A. 135
recharge of aquifers 28
red beet 31
redistribution of water in soil 64
reservoir 7, 26
resistance method for measuring soil moisture 57
rhizosphere 61
rhubarb 76
rice 7, 24
ring culture 85
root cap 72
root constant 105
root hair 71, 72
root pressure 82, 89, 91

root system 72
rose 31
Rothwell, J.B. 18
runoff 1
runoff measurement 67
ryegrass 87

Sale, J.M. 123
salinity 31
Salmonella 30
Salter, P.J. 46, 47, 49, 120, 135
salt tolerance of crops 31
saturated flow 65
Schofield, R.K. 39
Scholander, P.F. 94
seawater 29
Severn Estuary 29
shading 122
Shaw, R. 135
silicone 26
slaking 63
slurry, farmyard effluent 120
Smith, L.P. 111, 131
soil moisture deficit 106
soil moisture stress 7
soil moisture tension 50
soil reservoir 1
soil reservoir exploitation 122, 124
soil samples 60
soil structure 49, 121
soil texture 35, 121
soil water content measurement 50
solar distillation 30
solarimeter 13
spinach 31
spray irrigation 127
sprinkler irrigation 127
Stanhill, G. 110, 135
Steckel, J.R.A. 114, 115
stem flow 76
stem flow measurement 78
Stiles, W. 79
stomata 73, 74, 94
stomatal aperture measurement 76, 77
Stone, D.A. 48
storage of water 7
strain gauge lysimeter 20

strawberry 27, 31
structure of soil 49, 121
sugar beet 31, 88
sugar cane 72
sunflower 41, 42, 58, 59, 92
sunshine correction 109
surface wetness gauge 15, 16
Sykes, D.J. 41, 42

Tanner, C.B. 135
Taylor, J.A. 135
tea 1, 23, 72, 85, 122
tensiometer 54, 57, 124
tension 45
tension table 55
texture of soil 35, 121
texturing, hand 46
Thames Estuary 29
thermocouple psychrometer 57, 98
Thornthwaite, C.W. 102
thermal method for measuring soil moisture 57
tilth 8
tomato 32, 85, 116
transpiration 8, 91, 107
transpiration balance 108
transpiration cuticular 95
transpiration measurement 109
transpirometer 21
transplanting 85, 96
trickle irrigation 127
triangular diagram for classifying soil 38, 47
tulip 31
turnip 116

UK evaporation tank 17

US Class A evaporation pan 17
United States Department of Agriculture system of soil classification 36
unsaturated flow 66

Veihmeyer tube 60
vessels in the plant 71

Wash, The 29
water balance 7, 9, 11
water conservation 121
watercress 24, 30
water harvesting 121
watermelon 30
water need 9
water potential 93
water potential gradient 86
water saturation deficit 93
water stress 93, 113, 116, 118, 119
water table 43, 65, 121
Weatherley, P.E. 78, 98
weather recording 11
Webster, R. 54
weir, Vee-notch 32
well 26
Wesseling, J. 134
wheat 31
Wilkinson, B. 55
Williams, J.B. 46, 47
Williams, J.H. 31, 32
wilting 88
wilting point 41, 58
Winter, E.J. 17, 21, 110, 135

xylem 71

Zea mays 41

K₃